WeightWat

DINING
for TWO

150 EASY RECIPES
for EVERYDAY *and*
SPECIAL OCCASIONS

A Word About Weight Watchers

Since 1963, Weight Watchers has grown from a handful of people to millions of enrollments annually. Today, Weight Watchers is recognized as the leading name in safe and sensible weight control. Weight Watchers members form diverse groups, from youths to senior citizens, attending meetings virtually around the globe. Weight-loss and weight-management results vary by individual, but we recommend that you attend Weight Watchers meetings, follow the Weight Watchers food plan, and participate in regular physical activity. For the Weight Watcher meeting nearest you, call 800-651-6000. Also, check out *Weight Watchers* Magazine (for subscription information call 800-978-2400) and visit us at our web site: WeightWatchers.com

Weight Watchers Publishing Group

Creative and Editorial Director: **Nancy Gagliardi**
Art Director: **Ed Melnitsky**
Production Manager: **Alan Biederman**
Food Editor: **Eileen Runyan, M.S.**
Office Manager/Publishing Assistant: **Jenny Laboy-Brace**
Recipe Developers: **David Bonom, Cynthia DePersio, Lori Longbotham, Maureen Luchejko**
Food Consultant: **Deborah Mintcheff**
Nutrition Consultant: **Bea Krinke**
Photographer: **Rita Maas**
Food Styling: **William Smith**
Prop Styling: **Cathy Cook**
Designer: **Amy C. King**
On the Cover: **Crunchy Peanut Noodles, page 75 (with a *POINTS*® value of only *5*)**

Recipe Symbols:

🔥 SPICY   ⊗ NO COOK   🍳 ONE POT   🕐 20 MINUTES OR LESS

🌿 VEGETARIAN   🗑 PANTRY SHELF

INTRODUCTION

Cooking for two has always been an alien concept for me—and it's not because I come from a particularly large family. My issues probably have to do with the fact that I am descended from cooks whose recipes start with lines like, "Take 5 pounds of flour…" or "Separate a dozen eggs…" The thinking that has been passed down generation to generation in my home is that it's just as easy to cook for eight as it is for four.

This "more is better" school of cooking works great if unexpected guests are commonplace in your household or you live for leftovers. It's not so great, however, if you're trying to lose weight— when you consider that one of the key elements to weight loss is learning how to rethink your portions. How much you cook is directly related to the amount you put on a plate. And studies have shown that the amount you put on your plate is directly related to the amount you will eat.

Pair the portion part of the equation with the fact that the American family has changed dramatically in recent years. Today, there are families with kids, as well as families with a single parent and one or more kids, families with no kids (newlyweds, empty nesters, or just "no kids"), and families with an alternative to kids (think cats and dogs). Now factor in the schedule(s) of the new American family. Today, the reality is that no matter how big your brood, because of the crazy schedules, you can guarantee that the night will roll around when it's just two of you. And if you're used to cooking for many, cooking for one or two can be a surprising challenge.

Enter *Dining for Two*, the latest cookbook from Weight Watchers Publishing Group. We compiled 150 easy recipes to satisfy all your "dining for two" situations: brunches, lunches, light bites, entrées, and desserts. We've even included dishes for holidays and special occasions when you're celebrating "*à deux*," as well as recipes that leave you with delicious leftovers.

So whether you're in need of a meal that's just enough for two, or you want to learn what portions for two are really about, get cooking with *Dining for Two*.

Regards,
Nancy Gagliardi
Creative and Editorial Director

CONTENTS

——•——

1

LAID-BACK BRUNCHES

SIMPLE AND SPECIAL WEEKEND TREATS

Grilled Shrimp Caesar Salad

GRILLED SHRIMP CAESAR SALAD

MAKES 2 SERVINGS

If you love Caesar salad, here is a great way to take it from a simple side dish to a substantial and elegant brunch. The warm, just-off-the-grill shrimp is terrific on the crunchy salad, but if you want to save time, you can simply top the salad with store-bought cooked shrimp instead.

2   slices whole-grain bread, cut
     into ¾-inch cubes

Salt

Freshly ground pepper

1   small garlic clove

2   tablespoons reduced-sodium
     chicken broth

2   tablespoons freshly grated
     Parmesan cheese

1   tablespoon finely chopped
     flat-leaf parsley

1   teaspoon cider vinegar

½   teaspoon Dijon mustard

½   flat anchovy, mashed to a
     paste (optional)

1   tablespoon olive oil

½   pound large shrimp, peeled
     and deveined

1   small head romaine lettuce,
     shredded (4 cups)

1. Preheat the oven to 350°F. To make the croutons, place the bread cubes on a baking sheet, lightly spray with olive-oil nonstick spray, season with a pinch each of salt and pepper, and toss until coated. Bake, shaking the pan once, until golden brown, about 10 minutes. Set aside to cool.

2. To make the dressing, mash the garlic to a paste with a pinch of salt in a small bowl. Add broth, 1 tablespoon of the Parmesan cheese, the parsley, vinegar, mustard, and anchovy (if using); whisk until blended. Add the oil in a slow, steady steam and whisk until creamy.

3. Spray a nonstick ridged grill pan with nonstick spray and set over medium heat. Season the shrimp with a pinch each of salt and pepper; place in one layer in the grill pan. Cook until the shrimp are lightly browned on the outside and just opaque in center, about 2 minutes on each side.

4. Toss together the lettuce, dressing, croutons, and the remaining 1 tablespoon Parmesan cheese in a large bowl until combined. Divide the salad between 2 plates, top evenly with the shrimp, and serve at once.

Per serving (1 salad): 241 Cal, 11 g Fat, 3 g Sat Fat, 0 g Trans Fat, 112 mg Chol, 635 mg Sod, 17 g Carb, 4 g Fib, 19 g Prot, 175 mg Calc. *POINTS* value: *5.*

GRAND GRILLED CHICKEN WITH FRUIT AND RICOTTA TOPPING

MAKES 2 SERVINGS

The whipped ricotta topping is perfectly smooth, as creamy as whipped cream, and has a lovely sweetness from the ripe banana, making it a perfect foil for the peppery watercress and vibrant fresh fruits in this salad.

½ mango, peeled, seeded, and cut into ½-inch chunks

1 small wedge cantaloupe, cut into ½-inch chunks

5 strawberries, hulled and sliced

½ cup fresh blueberries or raspberries

2 (¼-pound) skinless boneless chicken breast halves

Pinch salt

Pinch cayenne

¼ ripe large banana, sliced

6 tablespoons part-skim ricotta cheese

¾ teaspoon sugar

½ teaspoon fresh lemon juice

⅛ teaspoon vanilla extract

1 bunch watercress, tough stems discarded

1. Combine the mango, cantaloupe, strawberries, and blueberries in a bowl. Refrigerate, covered, until ready to serve, or up to 4 hours.

2. Spray the grill rack with nonstick spray; prepare the grill. Or spray a nonstick ridged grill pan with nonstick spray and set over medium heat. Season the chicken with the salt and cayenne; place on the grill rack. Grill, turning frequently, until the chicken is cooked through, 10–12 minutes. Transfer the chicken to a plate to cool slightly, about 10 minutes.

3. Meanwhile, puree the banana, ricotta cheese, sugar, lemon juice, and vanilla in a mini food processor.

4. Line 2 plates with the watercress, then top each with a piece of warm chicken. Evenly spoon the fruit salad over the chicken, then evenly top each serving with a dollop of the whipped ricotta-cheese mixture. Serve at once.

Per serving (1 salad): 304 Cal, 8 g Fat, 3 g Sat Fat, 0 g Trans Fat, 83 mg Chol, 289 mg Sod, 27 g Carb, 4 g Fib, 32 g Prot, 216 mg Calc. *POINTS* value: *6.*

———————— ● ————————

TIP When you puree the ricotta mixture in the food processor, do it for a full 2 minutes—that's how long it takes to smooth out the graininess of the ricotta and make it totally silky. If you don't have a mini food processor, simply mash the mixture as smooth as possible with a fork.

VEGETABLE QUESADILLAS

MAKES 2 SERVINGS 🔥 🍳 🥕

An update on a grilled cheese and tomato sandwich, our version of this Mexican favorite is loaded with fresh vegetables and zingy flavors from fresh jalapeño, cilantro, and lime. For an extra-fiery taste, add a few dashes of hot pepper sauce or a dollop of hot store-bought salsa.

2   plum tomatoes, quartered lengthwise and thinly sliced crosswise

1   very small zucchini, quartered lengthwise and thinly sliced crosswise

⅓   yellow bell pepper, seeded and finely chopped

2   scallions, thinly sliced

1   jalapeño pepper, seeded and minced (wear gloves to prevent irritation)

1   tablespoon minced fresh cilantro

2   tablespoons fresh lime juice

¼   teaspoon finely grated lime zest

Pinch salt

Pinch cayenne

2   (8-inch) fat-free flour tortillas

½   cup shredded reduced-fat Monterey Jack cheese

2   tablespoons plain fat-free yogurt

Fresh cilantro sprigs (optional)

1. Combine the tomatoes, zucchini, bell pepper, scallions, jalapeño pepper, minced cilantro, lime juice, lime zest, salt, and cayenne in a bowl.

2. Heat a medium nonstick skillet over medium heat. Add a tortilla and heat until warm, 1–2 minutes. Flip the tortilla, and spoon half of the tomato mixture over half of the tortilla. Top with half of the cheese, fold the tortilla over the filling, and cook until the cheese has melted, 2–3 minutes. Transfer the quesadilla to a plate and keep warm in an oven on low heat. Repeat with the remaining tortilla, tomato mixture, and cheese, making a total of 2 quesadillas. Top each with 1 tablespoon of the yogurt and a cilantro sprig (if using).

Per serving (1 quesadilla with 1 tablespoon yogurt): 275 Cal, 7 g Fat, 4 g Sat Fat, 0 g Trans Fat, 19 mg Chol, 869 mg Sod, 41 g Carb, 3 g Fib, 14 g Prot, 307 mg Calc. *POINTS* **value:** *5.*

BRUNCH "RISOTTO" WITH APPLE AND GOLDEN RAISINS

MAKES 2 SERVINGS

This risotto uses apple cider (rather than the traditional chicken broth), which, along with apple and raisins, gives sweetness to this light midday dish. It's perfect for fall when apples and cider are at their best. You could even use pear cider or juice instead of the apple cider if you like. And maybe top the finished risotto with a sprinkling of brown sugar and toasted chopped pecans for an even sweeter taste (a half tablespoon of each on each serving would increase your *POINTS* value by 1).

2　cups apple cider or juice

½　cup water

1　tablespoon vegetable oil

¼　cup finely chopped fennel or celery

2　scallions, thinly sliced (white and green portions separate)

½　cup carnaroli or Arborio rice

¼　cup finely chopped unpeeled McIntosh apple

2　tablespoons golden raisins

¼　teaspoon salt

1　tablespoon light cream cheese (Neufchâtel)

1. Bring the cider and water to a boil in a small saucepan. Reduce the heat and keep at a simmer.

2. Heat the oil in a medium nonstick saucepan over medium heat. Add the fennel and the white part of the scallions. Cook, stirring frequently, until softened, about 7 minutes. Add the rice and cook, stirring, until it is lightly toasted, 2–3 minutes.

3. Reduce the heat to medium-low. Add ¼ cup of the cider mixture and stir until it is absorbed. Continue to add the cider mixture, ¼ cup at a time, stirring until it is absorbed before adding more, until the rice is just tender; add the apple, raisins, and salt with the last addition of cider. The cooking time should be about 20 minutes from the first addition of cider. Remove the pan from the heat, then stir in the cream cheese until it melts. Sprinkle with the green part of the scallions and serve at once.

Per serving (about 1 cup): 426 Cal, 9 g Fat, 2 g Sat Fat, 0 g Trans Fat, 6 mg Chol, 360 mg Sod, 83 g Carb, 3 g Fib, 6 g Prot, 76 mg Calc. *POINTS* value: *9.*

TIP　Save a few leaves from the fresh fennel for garnish.

Brunch "Risotto" with Apple
and Golden Raisins

EASIEST HUEVOS RANCHEROS

MAKES 2 SERVINGS

Haas avocados are particularly rich and creamy (you can recognize them by their dark, rough-textured skin) and they make a delicious accompaniment to this dish. Once avocado flesh is exposed to the air it discolors rapidly, so it's best to slice it just before you are ready to serve it. If you prefer to have the avocado ready ahead of time, a sprinkling of lemon or lime juice will help prevent discoloration.

2   (6-inch) corn tortillas

1   cup canned fat-free refried beans

1   teaspoon unsalted butter or vegetable oil

2   large eggs

¼   cup store-bought thick and chunky salsa, at room temperature

2   teaspoons fat-free sour cream

2   small sprigs fresh cilantro

¼   Haas avocado, peeled, seeded, and cut into thin slices

1. Preheat the oven to 350°F. Wrap the tortillas tightly in foil and warm them in the oven, about 5 minutes.

2. Heat the refried beans in a small heavy saucepan over medium-low heat, stirring frequently, until just hot; keep warm.

3. Melt the butter in a medium nonstick skillet over medium heat. One at a time, break the eggs into a saucer, then slip into the skillet. Reduce the heat and cook the eggs slowly until the whites are completely set and the yolks begin to thicken but are not hard, or turn the eggs to cook both sides.

4. Arrange a tortilla on each of 2 plates. In the center of each tortilla, place 1 tablespoon of the salsa, top with ½ cup warm refried beans, then an egg, another 1 tablespoon of the salsa, and finally with 1 teaspoon of the sour cream and the cilantro. Garnish with the avocado slices and serve at once.

Per serving (1 heuvo ranchero): 304 Cal, 12 g Fat, 4 g Sat Fat, 0 g Trans Fat, 217 mg Chol, 735 mg Sod, 36 g Carb, 9 g Fib, 15 g Prot, 135 mg Calc. *POINTS* value: *6.*

TIP To ripen hard avocados, place them in a paper bag for about three days.

MINI DUTCH BABIES

MAKES 2 SERVINGS

Something of a cross between a large puffed pancake and a popover, these tiny Dutch babies are served in their baking dishes with fresh berries on the side. Like a soufflé, they need to be served right out of the oven, so have any accompaniments ready. You can serve these with warm crisp turkey bacon on the side (2 slices will increase the *POINTS* value by 2).

3   tablespoons low-fat (1%) milk, at room temperature

1   large egg, at room temperature

1   tablespoon granulated sugar

3   tablespoons all-purpose flour

Pinch salt

1   teaspoon unsalted butter

2   teaspoons confectioners' sugar

1   cup mixed fresh or thawed frozen berries

2   lemon wedges

1. Arrange one rack on the middle rung of the oven, place a baking sheet on the same middle rack. Preheat the oven to 450°F.

2. To make the batter, combine the milk, egg, and granulated sugar in a blender. Add the flour and salt and blend just until combined; set aside.

3. Divide the butter between two 6-ounce glass custard cups and place on the baking sheet. Heat in the oven until the butter is melted, about 2 minutes. Remove the baking sheet from the oven and carefully tilt the custard cups to coat the sides. Pour the batter into the hot custard cups.

4. Bake until the Dutch babies are puffed and begin to brown on top, 8–10 minutes. Arrange each custard cup on a plate, then sprinkle each with 1 teaspoon confectioners' sugar. Arrange berries and lemon wedges on the side.

Per serving (1 Dutch baby with ½ cup berries): 175 Cal, 5 g Fat, 2 g Sat Fat, 0 g Trans Fat, 112 mg Chol, 187 mg Sod, 27 g Carb, 2 g Fib, 6 g Prot, 52 mg Calc. *POINTS* value: *4*.

TIP   It's best to have all of the ingredients for the batter at room temperature for this recipe—this encourages the batter to puff up evenly, then set in shape in the hot oven.

Banana-Stuffed French Toast

Banana-Stuffed French Toast

MAKES 2 SERVINGS ◷ ✦

You can make this with store-bought, sliced cinnamon-raisin bread, but we think it looks and tastes even better if you pick up cinnamon-raisin bread at the local bakery and slice it yourself. Whichever kind of bread you use, you can either remove the crusts or leave them on. Serve this hearty breakfast dish with a variety of your favorite fresh fruits.

2   tablespoons light cream cheese (Neufchâtel), at room temperature

4   (⅜-inch-thick) slices cinnmon-raisin bread

1   ripe medium banana, thinly sliced

¼   cup low-fat (1%) milk

1   large egg

¼   teaspoon vanilla extract

1   teaspoon unsalted butter

2   tablespoons maple syrup, warmed

6   fresh strawberries, hulled and sliced

1. Spread the cream cheese on the bread. Divide the banana over 2 slices of the bread and top each with a slice of the remaining bread.

2. Combine the milk, egg, and vanilla in a small shallow bowl; beat lightly with a fork.

3. Melt the butter in a large nonstick skillet over medium heat. Briefly dip the sandwiches, one at a time, into the egg mixture. Place both sandwiches in the skillet. Cook until golden brown, 3–4 minutes on each side. Place a stuffed French toast on each of 2 plates; top each with 1 tablespoon of the maple syrup and 3 of the sliced strawberries.

Per serving (1 stuffed French toast with toppings): 352 Cal, 11 g Fat, 5 g Sat Fat, 1 g Trans Fat, 124 mg Chol, 289 mg Sod, 56 g Carb, 4 g Fib, 10 g Prot, 114 mg Calc. *POINTS* value: *7.*

TIP   To warm the maple syrup, place it in a small custard cup and microwave on High for about 20 seconds. For a creamier taste, you can substitute fat-free half-and-half for the milk if you like.

BANANA-SOY PANCAKES

MAKES 2 SERVINGS

No one will ever guess there is soy flour in these delectable pancakes—their lighter-than-air texture, subtle pale yellow color, and delicate sweet flavor won't give away a thing. Soy flour (made from finely ground soybeans) is very high in protein and lower in carbohydrates than regular flour. You can find soy flour in health-food stores—choose the defatted variety to keep the fat and calories at bay. It is generally mixed with other flours in baking because it contains no gluten. Serve these rich pancakes with fresh fruit such as sliced nectarines and fresh ripe berries.

1   cup fat-free buttermilk

1   large egg

2   tablespoons packed light brown sugar

1   tablespoon vegetable oil

½   teaspoon vanilla extract

1   ripe medium banana, mashed with a fork

¾   cup all-purpose flour

¼   cup fat-free soy flour

1¼ teaspoons baking powder

¼   teaspoon baking soda

¼   teaspoon salt

1. Combine the buttermilk, egg, sugar, oil, and vanilla in a small bowl. Stir in the banana until blended.

2. Combine the all-purpose flour, soy flour, baking powder, baking soda, and salt in a medium bowl. Stir the buttermilk mixture into the flour mixture until just blended. The batter will be a little lumpy. Let the batter stand, about 5 minutes.

3. Spray a nonstick griddle or large skillet with nonstick spray and set over medium heat until a drop of water sizzles. Pour the batter by 4 generous ¼ cupfuls onto the griddle, and cook until the bubbles that form on top have burst and the undersides are golden brown, about 3 minutes. Flip and cook until golden brown, about 3 minutes longer. Repeat with remaining batter making a total of 8 pancakes, using more nonstick spray if necessary.

Per serving (4 pancakes): 471 Cal, 11 g Fat, 3 g Sat Fat, 0 g Trans Fat, 110 mg Chol, 926 mg Sod, 75 g Carb, 5 g Fib, 18 g Prot, 377 mg Calc. *POINTS* value: *10.*

———— • ————

TIP If you prefer to lower the *POINTS* value, serve only two or three of these pancakes per person. You can keep the remaining pancakes in the refrigerator for up to five days.

Oatmeal Pancakes with Easy Blueberry Sauce

MAKES 2 SERVINGS

These pancakes are a great way to start the day—and they are very versatile. You can use any favorite flavor yogurt and fruit juice. Peach yogurt and peach juice work deliciously with the blueberry sauce.

¾ cup fresh or thawed frozen blueberries

2 tablespoons confectioners' sugar

1 tablespoon water

Pinch cinnamon

½ teaspoon fresh lemon juice

1 cup old-fashioned rolled oats

1 tablespoon packed brown sugar

¾ teaspoon baking powder

¼ teaspoon baking soda

Pinch salt

½ cup low-fat plain or favorite flavor yogurt

⅓ cup apple juice or other fruit juice

1 large egg, lightly beaten

¼ teaspoon vanilla extract

1. To make the blueberry sauce, combine blueberries, confectioners' sugar, water, and cinnamon in a small saucepan. Cook, stirring occasionally, over medium heat until slightly thickened, about 5 minutes. Remove from the heat and stir in the lemon juice. Keep warm.

2. Place the oats, brown sugar, baking powder, baking soda, and salt in a food processor; pulse until the oats are finely ground. Transfer to a bowl and add the yogurt, apple juice, egg, and vanilla; stir until just blended. Let the batter stand 5 minutes.

3. Spray a nonstick griddle or large skillet with nonstick spray and heat over medium heat until a drop of water sizzles. Pour the batter by four ¼ cupfuls onto the griddle, and cook until the bubbles that form on the top have burst and the undersides are golden brown, about 4 minutes. Flip and cook until golden brown, 3–4 minutes longer. Repeat with the remaining batter making a total of 8 pancakes, using more nonstick spray if necessary. Serve the pancakes with the blueberry sauce.

Per serving (4 pancakes and ¼ cup blueberry sauce): 341 Cal, 6 g Fat, 2 g Sat Fat, 0 g Trans Fat, 110 mg Chol, 565 mg Sod, 59 g Carb, 6 g Fib, 13 g Prot, 261 mg Calc. *POINTS* value: 7.

TIP Blueberries contain more antioxidants than any other fruit and luckily there are terrific fresh or frozen blueberries available all year. When blueberries are in season (especially delectable tiny wild Maine blueberries), freeze them in a zip-close plastic bag so you can enjoy them year round.

JOHNNYCAKES WITH CHERRY SAUCE

MAKES 2 SERVINGS

These old-fashioned New England flat griddlecakes date back to the 1700s and are traditionally made with stone-ground cornmeal, which you can buy in health-food stores and some supermarkets.

1½ teaspoons unsalted butter or vegetable oil

1 cup fresh Bing cherries (6 ounces), pitted, or thawed frozen pitted cherries

1½ tablespoons packed light brown sugar

1 cup stone-ground yellow or white cornmeal

2 tablespoons granulated sugar

Pinch salt

1¼ cups boiling water

¼ cup low-fat (1%) milk, at room temperature

2 teaspoons vegetable oil

1. To make the cherry sauce, melt butter in a medium nonstick skillet over medium heat. Add the cherries and cook, stirring frequently, until they begin to release their juices, about 4 minutes. Add the brown sugar and bring to a boil. Reduce the heat and simmer, stirring, until the sugar dissolves and the juices thicken slightly, about 4 minutes. Remove skillet from heat, let cool slightly, and use at once. Or let sauce cool to room temperature.

2. To make the johnnycakes, combine the cornmeal, granulated sugar, and salt in a bowl. Add the boiling water and milk; stir until just blended.

3. Heat 1 teaspoon of the oil on a nonstick griddle or large skillet over medium-high heat until a drop of water sizzles. Pour the batter by four ¼ cupfuls and spread to 3-inch rounds. Cook until crisp and the undersides are golden brown, 5–6 minutes. Flip and cook until golden brown, 5–6 minutes longer. Repeat with the remaining oil and batter, making a total of 8 johnnycakes. Serve with the cherry sauce.

Per serving (4 johnnycakes and ⅓ cup cherry sauce): 470 Cal, 10 g Fat, 3 g Sat Fat, 0 g Trans Fat, 9 mg Chol, 164 mg Sod, 90 g Carb, 7 g Fib, 8 g Prot, 65 mg Calc. *POINTS* value: *9.*

TIP You can keep the sauce in the refrigerator, covered, for up to two days. Bring it to room temperature before using or reheat it gently and serve it warm.

IRISH OATMEAL WITH DRIED APRICOTS AND BROWN SUGAR

MAKES 2 SERVINGS

Irish oatmeal, Scotch oats, or steel-cut oats are all names for groats that have been cut into pieces but not rolled. They have an incredible nutty flavor and texture and are very much worth the extra time it takes to cook them—about 45 minutes. You can find them in health-food or natural-food stores. Don't use quick-cooking Irish oatmeal, old-fashioned rolled oats, or quick-cooking rolled oats in this recipe. Feel free to use whatever dried fruit you'd like—dried sour cherries, prunes, golden raisins, figs, currants, or pears would all work deliciously here. You may also like to top the oatmeal with sliced fresh fruit or berries.

1   cup water

1   cup apple cider or juice

½   (3-inch) cinnamon stick

2   teaspoons packed brown sugar

Pinch salt

½   cup Irish oatmeal

½   cup finely chopped
     dried apricots

½   cup low-fat (1%) milk,
     warmed

1. Bring the water, cider, cinnamon stick, 1 teaspoon of the sugar, and the salt to a boil in a heavy saucepan. Add the oatmeal and return to a boil. Reduce the heat and simmer, uncovered, stirring occasionally, for about 15 minutes.

2. Discard the cinnamon stick and continue simmering, stirring frequently, about 15 minutes longer. Stir in ¼ cup of the dried apricots and simmer, stirring frequently, about 15 minutes longer.

3. Transfer the oatmeal to 2 bowls. Top evenly with the remaining ¼ cup dried apricots, the remaining 1 teaspoon sugar, and the milk. Serve at once.

Per serving (¾ cup cooked oatmeal with toppings): 332 Cal, 3 g Fat, 1 g Sat Fat, 0 g Trans Fat, 2 mg Chol, 183 mg Sod, 69 g Carb, 7 g Fib, 10 g Prot, 125 mg Calc. *POINTS* value: *6.*

TIP Consider making a double batch of this oatmeal to reheat for almost-instant breakfasts later in the week.

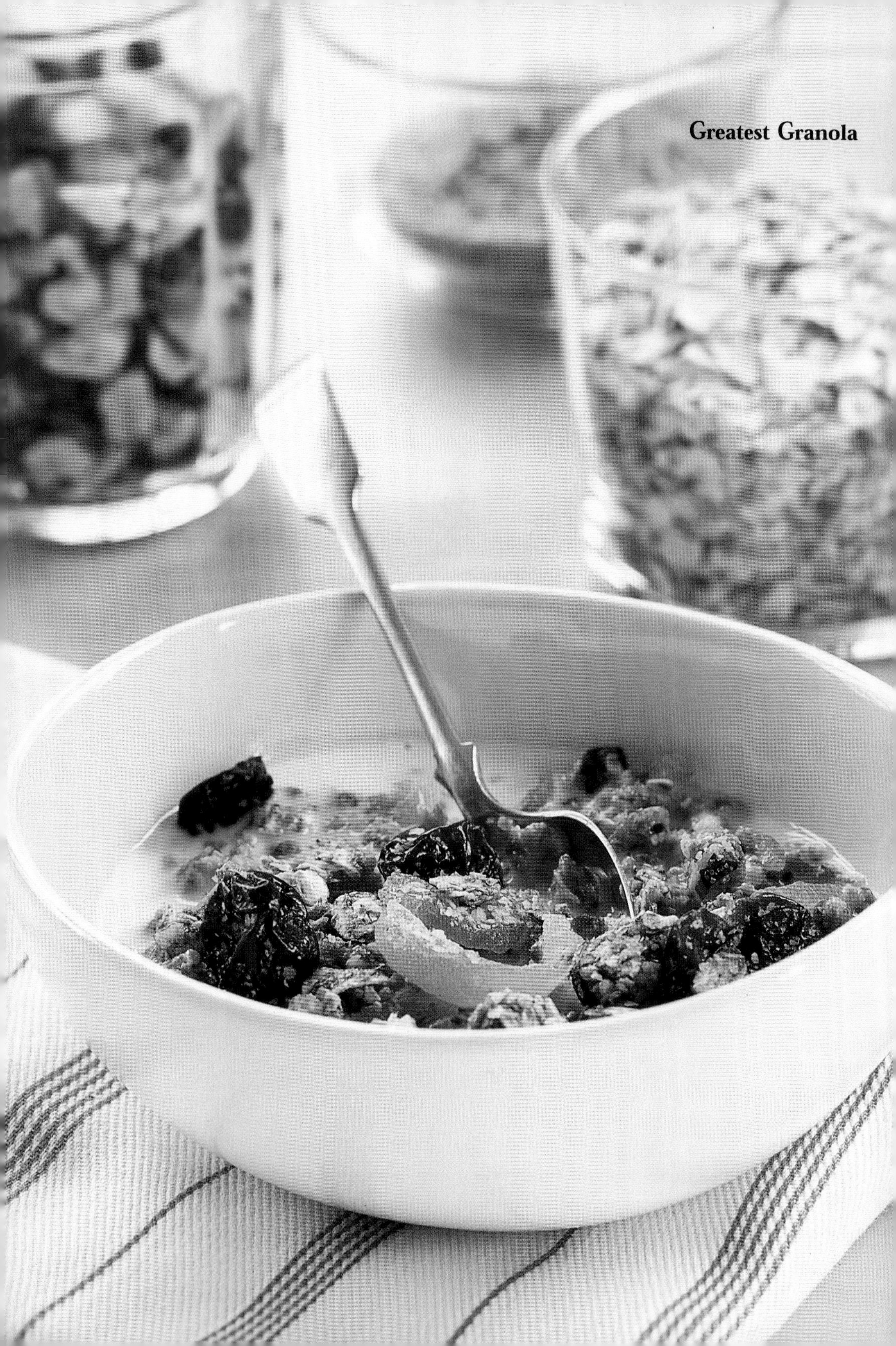

Greatest Granola

GREATEST GRANOLA

MAKES 10 SERVINGS

Granola sold in supermarkets is often loaded with fat and sugar. Our granola has no added oil or butter—*and* it contains a variety of healthful grains. Mixed rolled grains are available in health-food or natural-food stores and some large supermarkets. You'll up the *POINTS* value by 1 (and add a dose of protein and calcium), if you top each ½ cup serving of granola with about ½ cup warm low-fat (1%) or fat-free milk. It is also wonderful with sliced fresh strawberries, bananas, or raspberries.

1½ cups mixed rolled grains such as oats, wheat, or barley

½ cup unprocessed wheat bran

¼ cup sesame seeds

½ cup hazelnuts, coarsely chopped

6 tablespoons honey

½ teaspoon vanilla extract

¼ teaspoon pumpkin-pie spice or cinnamon

¾ cup thinly sliced dried peaches or apricots

½ cup dried sour cherries or golden raisins

¼ cup toasted wheat germ

1. Arrange one rack on the middle rung of the oven. Preheat the oven to 350°F.

2. Spread the rolled grains, bran, and sesame seeds on a baking sheet with a rim on all four sides. Bake, stirring with a metal spatula every 3 minutes, until the mixture is light golden brown, 9–10 minutes.

3. Meanwhile, combine the hazelnuts, honey, vanilla, and pumpkin-pie spice in a medium bowl. Add the grain mixture and toss to combine. Return the mixture to the baking sheet and spread evenly. Bake, stirring every 3 minutes, until dark golden brown, 9–10 minutes longer. Transfer the mixture to a bowl and let cool.

4. Combine the dried peaches, cherries, and wheat germ in a small bowl. Stir the dried fruit mixture into the toasted grain mixture.

Per serving (½ cup): 214 Cal, 7 g Fat, 1 g Sat Fat, 0 g Trans Fat, 0 mg Chol, 5 mg Sod, 36 g Carb, 5 g Fib, 6 g Prot, 32 mg Calc. *POINTS* value: *4.*

———————————————— • ————————————————

TIP Granola is best stored in a covered container in the refrigerator for up to three months or in the freezer for up to six months.

CHOCOLATE-HAZELNUT MUFFINS

MAKES 8 SERVINGS

Make these for a special weekend brunch for just the two of you or for guests. You can wrap and freeze any leftovers for another day. To round out the brunch, serve the muffins with fruit (try sliced pears and fresh blueberries), and a latte or a cappuccino. Or, if you really love chocolate, serve hot cocoa.

1½ cups all-purpose flour

½ cup unsweetened cocoa

1 teaspoon baking powder

½ teaspoon baking soda

¼ teaspoon salt

½ cup + 1 tablespoon packed dark brown sugar

8 tablespoons chopped toasted hazelnuts

1 cup chocolate low-fat (1%) milk

3 tablespoons vegetable oil

1. Preheat the oven to 350°F. Spray 8 of the cups in a 12-cup muffin tin with nonstick spray.

2. Combine the flour, cocoa, baking powder, baking soda, and salt in a medium bowl. Stir in the ½ cup sugar with a fork until no large lumps of cocoa remain. Stir in 6 tablespoons of the hazelnuts. Combine the milk and oil in a small bowl. Pour the milk mixture into the flour mixture; stir until just blended.

3. Combine the remaining 1 tablespoon sugar and the remaining 2 tablespoons hazelnuts in a small bowl.

4. Spoon the batter into the 8 muffin cups, filling each about two-thirds full. Sprinkle with the hazelnut and sugar mixture. Bake until a toothpick inserted in the center comes out clean, 20–25 minutes. Cool in the pan on a rack 2 minutes. Run a knife around the inside of the cups to release the muffins and cool on the rack. Serve warm or at room temperature.

Per serving (1 muffin): 266 Cal, 11 g Fat, 2 g Sat Fat, 0 g Trans Fat, 1 mg Chol, 240 mg Sod, 40 g Carb, 3 g Fib, 6 g Prot, 101 mg Calc. *POINTS* value: *6.*

───────────●───────────

TIP You might like to use 1¼ cups white whole-wheat flour instead of the 1½ cups all-purpose flour in this recipe. It is light-colored and mild tasting and has more fiber than regular white flour. It is available in most large supermarkets.

PUMPKIN-CHUTNEY BREAD

MAKES 10 SERVINGS

We tend to forget about pumpkin when it isn't Halloween or Thanksgiving, but since it has so much to offer nutritionally, you might consider making this year-round. Quick breads such as this are an easy way to prepare brunch ahead of time. Enjoy a slice of this bread (try it toasted) with a 2-ounce low-fat breakfast sausage (2 *POINTS* value) and a few fresh strawberries.

1½ cups all-purpose flour

⅔ cup packed dark brown sugar

1 teaspoon baking soda

1 teaspoon ground ginger

1 teaspoon cinnamon

½ teaspoon baking powder

½ teaspoon ground allspice

¼ teaspoon salt

1 cup canned pumpkin puree

1 (8½-ounce) jar mango chutney, large pieces chopped

¾ cup golden raisins

¼ cup chopped toasted pecans

1 large egg

2 egg whites

⅓ cup vanilla low-fat yogurt

¼ cup vegetable oil

1. Preheat the oven to 350°F. Lightly spray a 5 x 9-inch loaf pan with nonstick spray.

2. Combine the flour, sugar, baking soda, ginger, cinnamon, baking powder, allspice, and salt in a large bowl. Combine the pumpkin, chutney, raisins, pecans, egg, egg whites, yogurt, and oil in a small bowl. Add the pumpkin mixture to the flour mixture and stir with a rubber spatula until just blended.

3. Pour the batter into the loaf pan and bake until a toothpick inserted in the center comes out clean, 60–70 minutes. Cool the bread in the pan on a rack 10 minutes; remove from the pan and cool completely on the rack. Cut into 10 slices.

Per serving (1 slice): 287 Cal, 9 g Fat, 1 g Sat Fat, 0 g Trans Fat, 22 mg Chol, 254 mg Sod, 50 g Carb, 2 g Fib, 5 g Prot, 64 mg Calc. *POINTS* **value:** *6.*

TIP Quick breads are great to wrap in individual slices and have in the freezer, ready to thaw (microwave a slice on High about 30 seconds) for a quick brunch, breakfast, or teatime treat.

CHERRY-LIME SCONES

MAKES 6 SERVINGS

In England, scones are traditionally served with clotted cream or a thick pat of butter, both of which are very high in fat. We suggest serving this scone with a bowl of your favorite fat-free fruit-flavored yogurt (½ cup will raise the *POINTS* value by 2). You can freeze leftover scones in zip-close plastic bags, for up to a month. When ready, you can either thaw the scones in their bags on the counter overnight or remove the scones from their bags and warm them in a toaster oven.

1   cup all-purpose flour

1   tablespoon + 1 teaspoon sugar

1½ teaspoons baking powder

½   teaspoon salt

2   tablespoons vegetable oil

¼   cup + 1 teaspoon low-fat (1%) milk

3   tablespoons fat-free egg substitute

1½ teaspoon finely grated lime zest

⅓   cup dried sour cherries, chopped

1. Preheat the oven to 450°F.

2. Combine the flour, the 1 tablespoon sugar, the baking powder, and salt in a bowl. Stir in the oil with a fork until the mixture resembles coarse crumbs.

3. Combine the ¼ cup milk, the egg substitute, and lime zest in a small bowl. Add the milk mixture and the dried cherries to the flour mixture and stir until just blended. Gather the dough into a ball.

4. Lightly knead the dough on a lightly floured surface, about 1 minute. Pat dough into a circle about ½-inch thick. Brush with the remaining 1 teaspoon milk and sprinkle with the remaining 1 teaspoon sugar. Cut the dough into 6 pie-shaped pieces and arrange 1-inch apart on a baking sheet. Bake until golden brown, 10–12 minutes. Transfer the scones to a rack to cool slightly. The scones are best served warm.

Per serving (1 scone): 162 Cal, 5 g Fat, 1 g Sat Fat, 0 g Trans Fat, 0 mg Chol, 340 mg Sod, 26 g Carb, 1 g Fib, 4 g Prot, 91 mg Calc. *POINTS* value: *3*.

———————————— ● ————————————

TIP   Aromatic oils in lime zest add much flavor to food. The zest of the lime is the outermost, colored layer of the skin (without any of the bitter white pith underneath the skin). To remove the zest, rub the whole lime against the fine side of a grater until the zest is grated away.

Pumpkin-Chutney Bread (left)
Cherry-Lime Scones and
Chocolate-Hazelnut Muffins (in basket)

2

ON-THE-GO LUNCHES

QUICK AND PORTABLE
SANDWICHES, SOUPS, AND SALADS

CHICKEN AND PROSCIUTTO PAN BAGNA

MAKES 2 SERVINGS ✖ 🕐

Pan Bagna is a Mediterranean hero sandwich usually made with tuna. Here we stuff a hero loaf with flavorful sliced deli chicken, Italian prosciutto, roasted red pepper, and fresh basil. We recommend eating this sandwich the way they do in the Mediterranean—after the sandwich has been kept under a heavy weight in the refrigerator overnight and the flavors have mingled. If you can't wait and want to eat it right away, that's fine too.

¼ cup finely chopped red onion

4 small oil-cured black olives, pitted and chopped

1 tablespoon chopped fresh basil

2 teaspoons red-wine vinegar

2 teaspoons extra-virgin olive oil

1 (7-inch) crusty hero loaf

2 ounces thinly sliced deli chicken or turkey

1 ounce (2 slices) thinly sliced prosciutto

1 jarred roasted red pepper, cut into fourths

1. Combine the onion, olives, basil, vinegar, and oil in a small bowl.

2. Slice the hero loaf horizontally almost all the way through; spread open. Spread the onion mixture on both sides of the bread. Arrange chicken, prosciutto, and roasted red pepper on the bottom half of the loaf. Close the top of the loaf over the bottom, then cut the sandwich in two.

3. Eat the sandwiches at once or wrap in plastic wrap and put on a plate. Stand another plate on top and place in the refrigerator. Put a heavy can on top of the plate to weigh the sandwiches down and refrigerate for up to 24 hours.

Per serving (½ sandwich): 309 Cal, 11 g Fat, 2 g Sat Fat, 0 g Trans Fat, 16 mg Chol, 1108 mg Sod, 38 g Carb, 3 g Fib, 13 g Prot, 46 mg Calc. *POINTS* value: *6.*

———————— • ————————

TIP The small amount of prosciutto adds full, rich flavor to the sandwich. For best flavor, choose prosciutto imported from Italy such as prosciutto di Parma, also called Parma ham.

Tex-Mex Tuna Wraps

MAKES 2 SERVINGS ✖ 🕐

Want to get out of the fast-food lunch rut? There's nothing easier than a sandwich to pack, and when the sandwich is a trendy wrap, tastes this good, and keeps this well overnight, you'll make it again and again. If you like, you can substitute 4 slices of toasted multi-grain bread for the 2 tortillas. If you do, you will step up the per-serving *POINTS* value by 1.

1   (6-ounce) can solid white tuna packed in water, drained and flaked

½   cup finely chopped yellow bell pepper

2   scallions, thinly sliced (white and light green portions only)

¼   cup tomato salsa

2   tablespoons chopped fresh cilantro

4   teaspoons low-fat mayonnaise

2   (6-inch) fat-free flour tortillas

½   cup loosely packed fresh baby spinach leaves or 2 romaine lettuce leaves

1. Combine the tuna, bell pepper, scallions, salsa, and cilantro in a bowl.

2. Spread 2 teaspoons of the mayonnaise over each tortilla. Top with the tuna mixture, then the spinach leaves. Roll up the tortillas, cut each in half, and serve at once. Or wrap in plastic wrap and refrigerate for up to 24 hours.

Per serving (1 wrap): 215 Cal, 2 g Fat, 0 g Sat Fat, 0 g Trans Fat, 23 mg Chol, 764 mg Sod, 26 g Carb, 2 g Fib, 23 g Prot, 70 mg Calc. *POINTS* value: *4.*

──────────── ● ────────────

TIP   If you have fresh cilantro that you don't think you'll be using soon, chop and freeze it in 2-tablespoon portions in small zip-close freezer bags. It will thaw in a few minutes on a counter. You'll find a tablespoon or two gives a fresh Mexican taste when added to a favorite jarred salsa or sprinkled in a quesadilla.

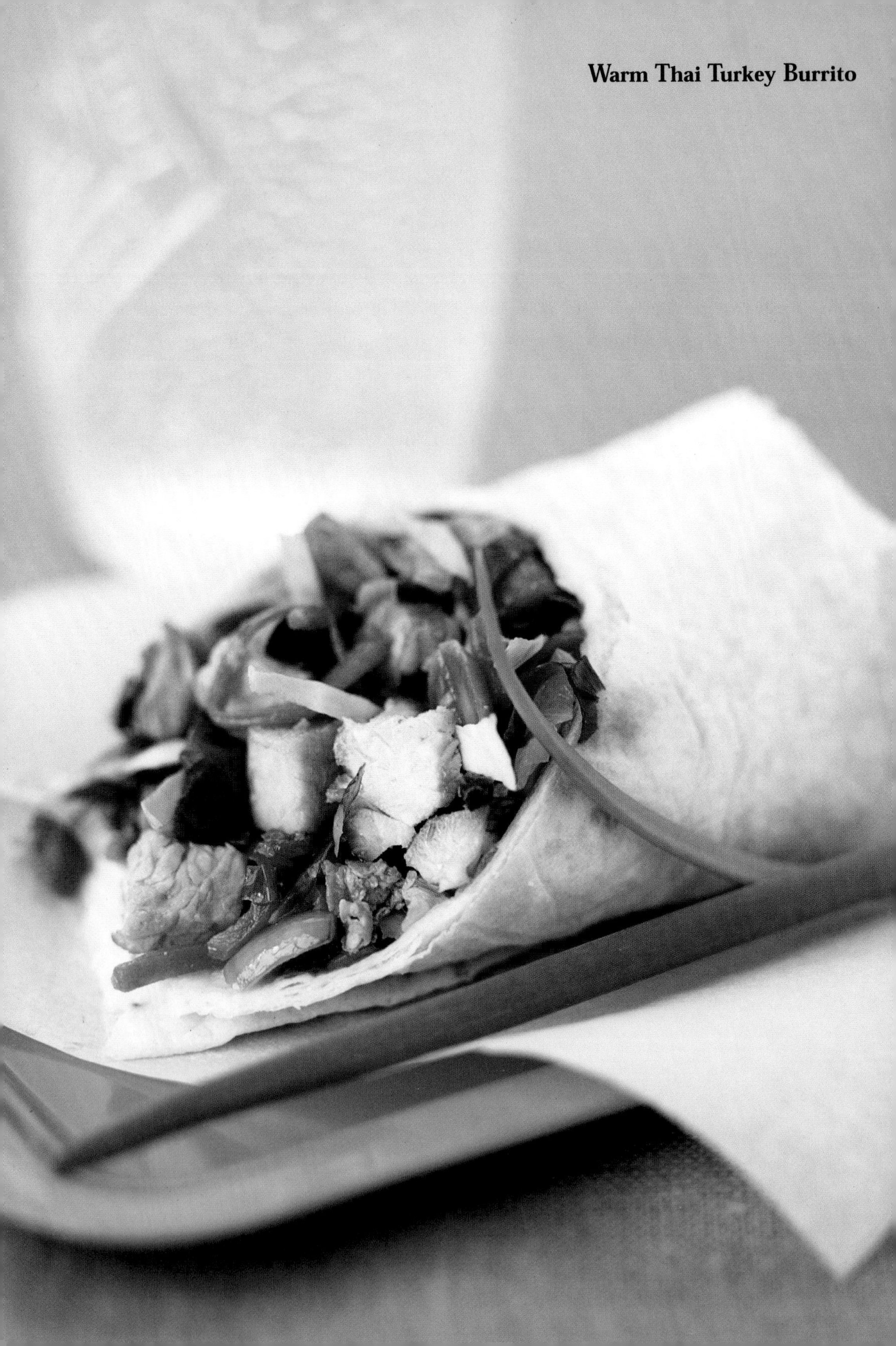
Warm Thai Turkey Burrito

Warm Thai Turkey Burrito

MAKES 2 SERVINGS ♦ ⌐ ◔

To keep this lunch easy to prepare, we use packaged coleslaw mix (available in the produce aisle of the supermarket) instead of shredding cabbage and carrots. This is a great way to use leftover cooked turkey or chicken if you have it. Or buy ¼ pound of sliced turkey or chicken from the deli counter and chop it—just be aware that deli turkey and chicken tend to be fairly high in salt.

1	teaspoon Asian (dark) sesame oil
2	cups packaged coleslaw mix
4	scallions, sliced
⅛	teaspoon crushed red pepper
1	cup finely chopped cooked turkey or chicken
2	tablespoons chopped unsalted dry-roasted peanuts
2	teaspoons fresh lime juice
1	teaspoon reduced-sodium soy sauce
2	tablespoons chopped fresh basil
1	(10-inch) burrito-size fat-free flour tortilla, warmed

1. Heat the oil in a large nonstick skillet over medium-high heat. Add the coleslaw mix, scallions, and crushed red pepper; cook, stirring frequently, until the cabbage begins to wilt, about 3 minutes.

2. Stir in the turkey, peanuts, lime juice, and soy sauce. Cook stirring frequently, until heated through, about 3 minutes. Stir in the basil.

3. Spoon the filling onto the tortilla and roll up. Cut the roll in half on a slight diagonal. Serve at once or pack for lunch (see TIP).

Per serving (½ burrito): 336 Cal, 10 g Fat, 2 g Sat Fat, 0 g Trans Fat, 57 mg Chol, 522 mg Sod, 33 g Carb, 4 g Fib, 28 g Prot, 117 mg Calc. *POINTS* value: *7.*

TIP To pack these rolls, let the filling cool, then fill the tortilla and roll up. Cut the tortilla in half and wrap the two halves separately in wax paper and keep refrigerated for up to 24 hours. Eat cold or microwave each roll half, in the wax paper wrapping, on High until heated through, about 1½ minutes.

BLT Pizza

MAKES 2 SERVINGS 🍲 ⏱

The blend of Italian cheeses gives good flavor to this pizza, but you can use part-skim mozzarella if you like. To keep it easy, buy microwave-ready, cooked bacon that needs only a brief turn in the microwave (follow package directions) to freshen and warm it.

1   (6-inch) individual prebaked pizza crust (from an 8-ounce two-crust package)

1   large tomato, thinly sliced

½   cup shredded light Italian 4-cheese blend (mozzarella, provolone, Asiago, and Romano)

¼   cup finely chopped radishes

1   teaspoon low-fat mayonnaise

1   teaspoon fresh lemon juice

1   cup shredded romaine lettuce

2   strips bacon, cooked crisp and crumbled

1. Preheat the oven to 475°F.

2. Split the pizza crust horizontally to make 2 rounds; place on a baking sheet. Arrange the tomato slices on top of the crusts. Sprinkle the cheese evenly over the tomatoes. Bake until heated through and the cheese melts, about 5 minutes.

3. Meanwhile, combine the radishes, mayonnaise, and lemon juice in a medium bowl; stir in the lettuce. Transfer the pizzas to 2 serving plates. Spoon the lettuce mixture evenly over the pizzas. Sprinkle evenly with the bacon and serve at once.

Per serving (1 pizza): 299 Cal, 11 g Fat, 5 g Sat Fat, 0 g Trans Fat, 22 mg Chol, 591 mg Sod, 36 g Carb, 3 g Fib, 13 g Prot, 196 mg Calc. *POINTS* value: *6.*

———————————⚫———————————

TIP If you prefer, don't split the crusts horizontally. Simply bake the tomato and cheese on the pizza crust, until heated through, about 10 minutes. Then sprinkle the lettuce mixture and bacon on the pizza and cut in half crosswise. Serve a half pizza per person.

BLT Pizza

AEGEAN SALAD PITAS

MAKES 2 SERVINGS ⊗ ⊙ ⚹

Enjoy a welcome change of pace from the standard Greek salad with pita bread on the side by serving this simple sandwich. Added bonus—it's easily packed for lunch at the office. To prevent the salad greens from wilting, make the sandwich in the morning no more than four to six hours before you plan on eating it. (You can complete step 1 the night before and finish making the sandwiches the next morning.) Use any hummus, such as original or roasted red pepper instead of the sun-dried tomato hummus, if you prefer.

1	plum tomato, chopped
½	cup chopped seedless cucumber
1	scallion, thinly sliced
1	tablespoon chopped fresh dill
1	teaspoon fresh lemon juice
1	(6-inch) whole-wheat pita bread
2	tablespoons sun-dried tomato hummus
1	cup loosely packed Mediterranean-blend bagged salad greens
2	ounces feta cheese, crumbled

1. Combine the tomato, cucumber, scallion, dill, and lemon juice in a medium bowl; set aside.
2. Split the pita bread crosswise to form 2 pockets. Spread 1 tablespoon of the hummus inside each pocket.
3. Gently stir the salad greens and feta cheese into the tomato mixture. Spoon evenly into the 2 pita pockets. Serve at once or wrap in plastic wrap and refrigerate for up to 6 hours.

Per serving (½ stuffed pita): 213 Cal, 8 g Fat, 4 g Sat Fat, 0 g Trans Fat, 25 mg Chol, 555 mg Sod, 27 g Carb, 5 g Fib, 10 g Prot, 190 mg Calc. *POINTS* value: *4*.

———————— • ————————

TIP   Substitute reduced-fat feta cheese for the regular feta cheese and lower the per-serving *POINTS* value by 1.

TORTILLA BEAN SOUP

MAKES 2 SERVINGS

Got a date for a hockey or football game? Then tote this soup in a thermos container to warm you both at half time. You'll need a thermos that holds a quart of liquid. Pack the tortilla chips separately in a zip-close plastic bag to sprinkle on the soup at the last minute. There are many varieties of salsas available in supermarkets today. Choose your favorite (not fruit-based for this recipe) or follow our lead and use a chunky corn, bean, and roasted red pepper salsa.

1   teaspoon canola oil

1   medium zucchini, diced

3   scallions, thinly sliced

1   (14-ounce) can reduced-sodium vegetable broth

1   (15½-ounce) can pinto beans, rinsed and drained

¼   cup corn, black bean, and roasted red pepper salsa

2   tablespoons chopped fresh cilantro or parsley

½   cup baked tortilla chips, broken up

1. Heat the oil in a medium saucepan over medium-high heat. Add the zucchini and scallions and cook, stirring frequently, until softened, about 3 minutes.

2. Add the broth, beans, and salsa; bring to a boil. Reduce the heat and simmer, uncovered, until the flavors blend, about 3 minutes. Stir in the cilantro. Divide the soup evenly between 2 bowls, sprinkle with the tortilla chips, and serve at once.

Per serving (2 cups): 308 Cal, 4 g Fat, 1 g Sat Fat, 0 g Trans Fat, 0 mg Chol, 832 mg Sod, 50 g Carb, 16 g Fib, 19 g Prot, 121 mg Calc. *POINTS* value: *6.*

———————————————— • ————————————————

TIP This recipe is easily doubled and kept refrigerated for up to five days, ready to reheat for a quick lunch or late-night supper.

Manhattan Clam Chowder

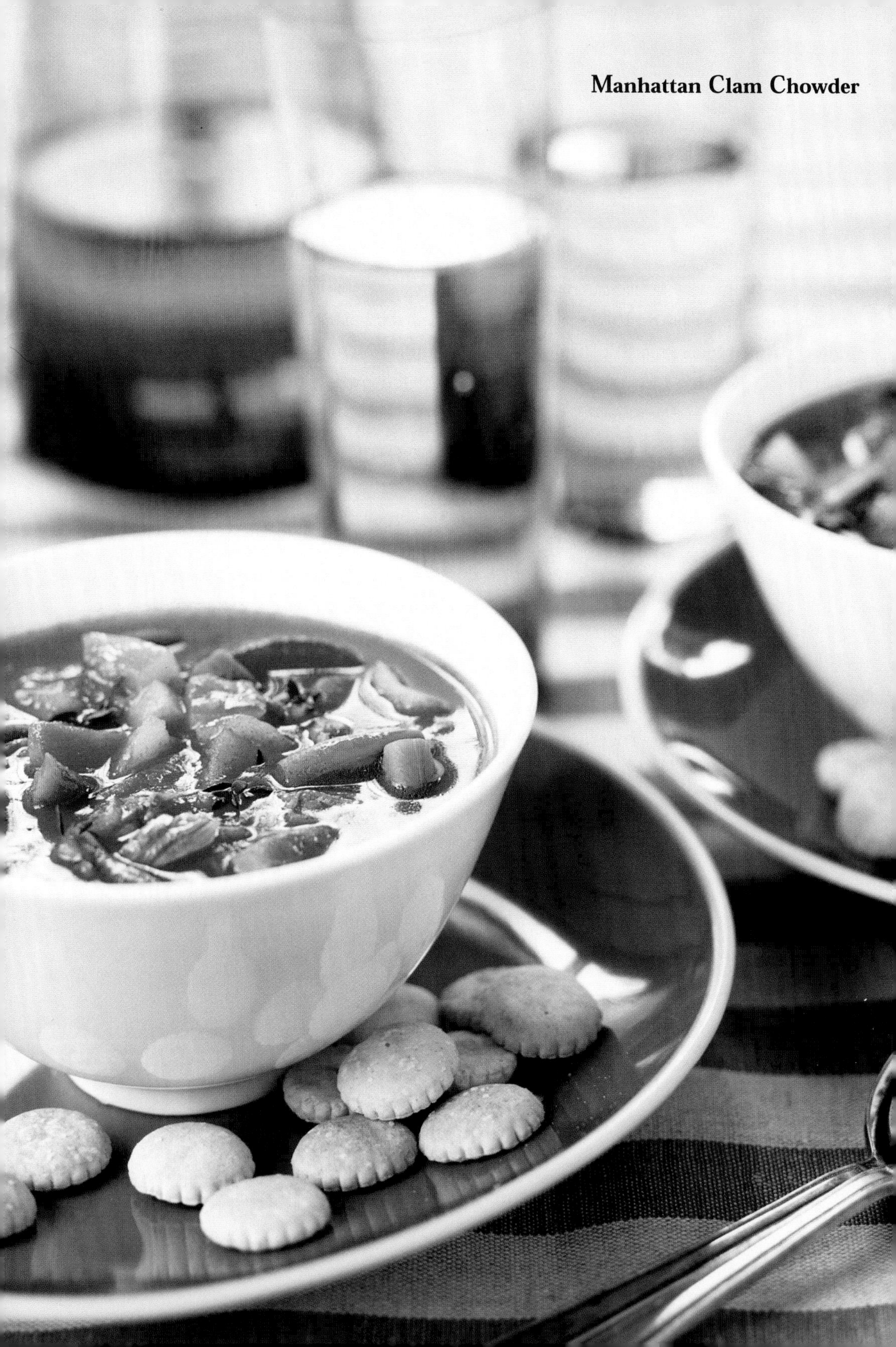

MANHATTAN CLAM CHOWDER

MAKES 2 SERVINGS

If this soup is a favorite of yours, keep these few everyday ingredients in your pantry or freezer. You'll be ready to whip it up at a moment's notice. Irish-style bacon, made from pork loin, is very lean and full of flavor. If you can't find it, use Canadian bacon. For a no-meat chowder, try adding a 1-inch square piece of Parmesan cheese to the simmering soup to give it depth of flavor. If you like, serve with a few oyster crackers—¼ cup will increase the *POINTS* value by 1.

1   small onion, chopped

1   (1-ounce) slice lean Irish-style bacon, cut into ¼-inch pieces

1   carrot, diced

1   (14½-ounce) can sliced stewed tomatoes

1   cup bottled clam juice or fish broth

1   medium (6-ounce) baking potato scrubbed and diced

1   bay leaf

½   (9-ounce) package frozen cut green beans

⅛   teaspoon freshly ground pepper

1   (10-ounce) can whole baby clams in juice

1   teaspoon finely chopped fresh thyme, or ¼ teaspoon dried

1. Spray a medium nonstick saucepan with nonstick spray and set over medium heat. Add the onion, bacon, and carrot and cook, stirring occasionally, until golden, about 8 minutes.

2. Add the tomatoes, clam juice, potato, and bay leaf; bring to a boil. Reduce the heat and simmer, covered, until the potatoes are tender, about 15 minutes.

3. Add the green beans and pepper; return to a boil. Reduce the heat and simmer, covered, until the beans are tender, about 3 minutes. Add the clams and their juice and cook until just heated through, about 2 minutes. Discard the bay leaf and stir in the thyme.

Per serving (generous 2 cups): 302 Cal, 3 g Fat, 1 g Sat Fat, 0 g Trans Fat, 56 mg Chol, 1201 mg Sod, 45 g Carb, 7 g Fib, 25 g Prot, 185 mg Calc. *POINTS* value: *5.*

TIP   You can easily double this recipe and refrigerate or freeze half in two (2-cup) containers ready to tote for lunch another day.

Chicken Avgolemono Soup with
Chicken and Prosciutto Pan Bagna, page 32

Chicken Avgolemono Soup

MAKES 2 SERVINGS 🍴 🕐 🥫

This light Greek favorite is made into a substantial meal by the addition of chicken. For a finishing touch, cut a toasted large pita bread into 8 wedges and serve alongside. You'll be increasing the per-serving *POINTS* value by 1.

1 teaspoon olive oil

2 shallots or 1 small onion, chopped

3 cups reduced-sodium chicken broth

⅓ cup orzo or other tiny pasta

¾ cup chopped cooked chicken

1 large egg

2 tablespoons fresh lemon juice

1 tablespoon chopped fresh parsley

Freshly ground pepper, to taste

1. Heat the oil in a medium saucepan over medium heat. Add the shallots and cook, stirring frequently, until golden, about 4 minutes.

2. Add the broth and orzo; bring to a boil. Reduce the heat and simmer, covered, until the orzo is tender, about 10 minutes. Stir in the chicken and simmer until heated through, about 1 minute.

3. Meanwhile, in a small bowl, lightly beat the egg and lemon juice. Stir about 2 tablespoons of the hot broth into the egg mixture. Gradually pour the egg mixture into the simmering soup and cook, stirring constantly, until the egg forms shreds, about 1 minute. Serve, sprinkled with the parsley and pepper.

Per serving (scant 2 cups): 307 Cal, 11 g Fat, 3 g Sat Fat, 0 g Trans Fat, 151 mg Chol, 806 mg Sod, 21 g Carb, 2 g Fib, 28 g Prot, 62 mg Calc. *POINTS* value: 7.

———————————•———————————

TIP If this soup and sandwich combo appeals to you, eat a quarter of the Chicken and Prosciutto Pan Bagna and a scant cup of the Chicken Avgolemono Soup.

CREAMY TORTELLINI AND VEGETABLE SALAD

MAKES 2 SERVINGS 🍲 🕐 🥕 🥫

We make this with frozen tortellini, but if you like you can use half of a 9-ounce package of fresh refrigerated tortellini (the mushroom and cheese version is tasty), which you can keep stored in your own refrigerator until its expiration date or in your freezer for up to three months. You can substitute ½ cup of chopped plum tomatoes for the cherry tomatoes, and shallots, scallions, or yellow onion for the red onion, if that's what's in your pantry.

¼ (1-pound) package frozen cheese tortellini

½ (10-ounce) package frozen sugar snap peas, thawed

1 tablespoon low-fat mayonnaise

1 tablespoon white balsamic vinegar

3 tablespoons grated Parmesan cheese

12 cherry tomatoes, cut in half

2 tablespoons finely chopped red onion

1 tablespoon capers, rinsed and drained

Freshly ground pepper

1. Cook the tortellini according to package directions, adding the sugar snap peas during the last 2 minutes of cooking. Drain and rinse under cold water until cooled slightly; set aside.

2. Meanwhile, combine the mayonnaise, vinegar, and 1 tablespoon of the Parmesan cheese in the bottom of a serving bowl. Add the tortellini and sugar snap peas, the tomatoes, onion, and capers; toss gently to coat. Sprinkle the salad with the remaining 2 tablespoons Parmesan cheese and the pepper. Serve at once or cover and refrigerate for up to 24 hours and serve chilled.

Per serving (1½ cups): 202 Cal, 8 g Fat, 4 g Sat Fat, 0 g Trans Fat, 55 mg Chol, 400 mg Sod, 23 g Carb, 4 g Fib, 11 g Prot, 204 mg Calc. *POINTS* **value:** *4.*

———————————— • ————————————

TIP Forgo the last 2 tablespoons of Parmesan cheese sprinkled on top of the salad and reduce the per-serving *POINTS* value by 1.

Creamy Tortellini and Vegetable Salad

ASIAN PORK AND CABBAGE SLAW

MAKES 2 SERVINGS ⊗ ⊗

This crisp, light salad is a perfect way to use leftover pork and it can be on the table in minutes. If you like, substitute leftover beef, turkey, or chicken for the chopped cooked pork. If you mix this salad the night before, you'll find that, though the salad is not quite as crisp by lunch time, the flavors are wonderfully melded. Serve each portion with 8 small, thin rice crackers and up the *POINTS* value by 1.

1   tablespoon rice-wine vinegar

2   teaspoons grated peeled
    fresh ginger

2   teaspoons reduced-sodium
    soy sauce

1   teaspoon Asian (dark)
    sesame oil

1   teaspoon honey

2   cups packaged coleslaw mix

1   cup finely chopped
    cooked pork

2   scallions, thinly sliced
    diagonally (white and light
    green portions only)

Mix together the vinegar, ginger, soy sauce, sesame oil, and honey in a medium bowl. Add the coleslaw mix, pork, and scallions; toss to coat.

Per serving (1½ cups): 205 Cal, 9 g Fat, 3 g Sat Fat, 0 g Trans Fat, 56 mg Chol, 227 mg Sod, 10 g Carb, 2 g Fib, 21 g Prot, 51 mg Calc. *POINTS* value: *4*.

———————————•———————————

TIP If you are toting this slaw to the office for lunch, pack a serving into a container and keep refrigerated until ready to eat. It will keep for up to 24 hours.

**Asian Pork and
Cabbage Slaw**

BARLEY TABBOULEH WITH CHICKPEAS

MAKES 2 SERVINGS 🍲 🕐 🌶

Tabbouleh is a Middle Eastern salad traditionally made with bulgur. For a change of pace, we use barley instead of bulgur and add chickpeas, plenty of vegetables, and feta cheese to make it a complete lunch. This recipe is easily doubled and keeps well in the refrigerator for up to four days— perfect for packing for lunch and a sure-fire way of ensuring you keep on track in the middle of the day. Substitute mint for parsley if you like.

⅔ cup reduced-sodium vegetable broth

⅓ cup quick-cooking barley

1 (7 ¾-ounce) can chickpeas, rinsed and drained

½ yellow bell pepper, seeded and diced

12 grape tomatoes, halved

⅓ cup finely chopped flat-leaf parsley

⅓ cup chopped red onion

1 tablespoon fresh lemon juice

1 teaspoon extra-virgin olive oil

⅛ teaspoon coarsely ground pepper

1 ounce reduced-fat feta cheese, crumbled

1. Bring the broth to a boil in a medium saucepan. Stir in the barley. Reduce the heat and simmer, covered, until the barley is softened, 10–12 minutes. Remove from the heat and let stand 5 minutes. Transfer the barley to a large bowl.

2. Add the chickpeas, bell pepper, tomatoes, parsley, onion, lemon juice, oil, and pepper; toss to combine. Sprinkle the salad with the feta cheese and serve while still slightly warm. Or cover and refrigerate for up to 4 days and serve chilled.

Per serving (1½ cups): 341 Cal, 7 g Fat, 2 g Sat Fat, 0 g Trans Fat, 6 mg Chol, 510 mg Sod, 57 g Carb, 13 g Fib, 16 g Prot, 158 mg Calc. *POINTS* value: *7.*

———————————————— • ————————————————

TIP Omit the feta cheese and lower the per-serving *POINTS* value by 1.

RED BEAN CHILI

MAKES 6 SERVINGS 🔥 🍲 🌶 🥫

Whether you're making chili for two people or a crowd, it's always worth making extra so you can enjoy it again (it's even better reheated). This makes about 6 cups of chili and if it *is* just the two of you, you can pack the 4 cups of leftover chili in 2-cup containers and refrigerate for up to five days or freeze for up to six months. Allspice adds a subtle sweet and spicy flavor, making for a nice change of pace.

2   teaspoons olive oil

1   large onion, chopped

3   garlic cloves, minced

1   (28-ounce) can diced tomatoes

2   (15½-ounce) cans red kidney
    beans, rinsed and drained

½   (1-pound) bag frozen mixed
    bell pepper strips

2   tablespoons canned chopped
    green chiles

2   tablespoons taco or chili
    seasoning mix

½   teaspoon ground allspice

1. Heat the oil in a nonstick Dutch oven over medium-high heat. Add the onion and garlic and cook, stirring frequently, until golden, 7–10 minutes.

2. Add tomatoes, beans, bell peppers, chiles, seasoning mix, and allspice; bring to a boil. Reduce the heat and simmer, uncovered, stirring occasionally until the chili is thickened, about 30 minutes.

Per serving (1 cup): 201 Cal, 2 g Fat, 0 g Sat Fat, 0 g Trans Fat, 0 mg Chol, 602 mg Sod, 36 g Carb, 9 g Fib, 11 g Prot, 91 mg Calc. *POINTS* value: *3*.

———————————————•———————————————

TIP You can serve the chili with rice (½ cup will boost the *POINTS* value by 2), or in taco shells, topped with shredded cheddar cheese and chopped scallions (1 taco shell and 2 tablespoons reduced-fat cheddar will boost the *POINTS* value by 2).

ORANGE AND LEMON HAM SALAD

MAKES 2 SERVINGS ⊗ ⊕

Ham goes well with many fruits. If you like, substitute fresh pineapple or mango chunks for the orange segments. Or, if you make this in late fall or winter when persimmons and pomegranates are available, try topping the salad with sliced peeled persimmon and a few pomegranate seeds. Add to the southern feeling and serve this salad with minted iced tea.

1   tablespoon fresh lemon juice

1   teaspoon canola oil

1   teaspoon Dijon mustard

1   teaspoon honey

1   Belgian endive, cut crosswise into ½-inch slices, then separated into pieces

2   cups baby spinach leaves

1   (¼-pound) piece fully cooked ham steak, cut into ¼-inch chunks

1   navel orange, peeled and cut into segments

½   cup fat-free croutons

2   tablespoons toasted chopped pecans

1. Combine the lemon juice, oil, mustard, and honey in the bottom of a medium salad bowl. Add the Belgian endive, spinach, and ham; toss to coat.

2. Arrange the salad on 2 plates. Top each salad evenly with the orange segments, croutons, and pecans. Serve at once.

Per serving (generous 2 cups): 250 Cal, 13 g Fat, 2 g Sat Fat, 0 g Trans Fat, 28 mg Chol, 878 mg Sod, 21 g Carb, 6 g Fib, 15 g Prot, 120 mg Calc. *POINTS* value: *5.*

APPLE AND WALNUT BRAN MUFFINS

MAKES 12 SERVINGS 🌱 🗑

Tired of oversized, high-fat deli muffins? These delicious, nutritious muffins are your answer—and they keep well in the freezer. Simply place the muffins in individual zip-close freezer bags and freeze for up to three months, ready to grab one in the morning as you leave for work for an on-the-go lunch or breakfast. To warm, simply remove the frozen muffin from its bag and microwave on High for 30 seconds. Or eat at room temperature. For a hearty lunch, serve with a 1-ounce wedge of reduced-fat sharp cheddar cheese and up the *POINTS* value by 2.

5	tablespoons packed light brown sugar
3	tablespoons finely chopped walnuts
2	large eggs
1¼	cups all-bran cereal
1	cup fat-free buttermilk or milk
2	tablespoons canola oil
2	tablespoons molasses
1	cup all-purpose flour
¼	cup toasted wheat germ
2	teaspoons baking powder
1	teaspoon cinnamon
½	teaspoon baking soda
¼	teaspoon salt
1	large apple, peeled, cored, and shredded

1. Preheat the oven to 375°F. Spray a nonstick 12-cup muffin tin with nonstick spray.

2. Mix 1 tablespoon of the brown sugar with 1 tablespoon of the walnuts in a small bowl; set aside for the topping.

3. Lightly beat the eggs in a large bowl. Add remaining 4 tablespoons brown sugar, the bran cereal, buttermilk, oil, and molasses; let soak 5 minutes.

4. Meanwhile, combine the flour, wheat germ, baking powder, cinnamon, baking soda, and salt in a medium bowl. Stir the flour mixture into the cereal mixture just until blended. Stir in the apple and the remaining 2 tablespoons walnuts.

5. Spoon the batter into the cups. Sprinkle the brown sugar and walnut topping evenly over the muffins. Bake until a toothpick inserted in a muffin comes out clean, 20–23 minutes. Cool in the pan on a rack 5 minutes. Remove from the pan and cool completely on the rack.

Per serving (1 muffin): 154 Cal, 5 g Fat, 1 g Sat Fat, 0 g Trans Fat, 36 mg Chol, 250 mg Sod, 24 g Carb, 2 g Fib, 4 g Prot, 94 mg Calc. *POINTS* value: *3.*

SAUSAGE AND SPINACH ROLLS

MAKES 4 SERVINGS

These light and crisp "strudels" are fun and easy to make as a couple. One person can handle the phyllo while the other person deals with the filling. You can save two of the rolls to pack for an office lunch or a quick bite at home another day. Simply let the rolls cool to room temperature, then wrap in foil and refrigerate for up to three days. Then, serve them cold or reheat in a preheated 375°F oven until heated through, 20 to 25 minutes. Or freeze the rolls for up to three months and bake directly from the freezer, in a preheated 350°F oven until heated through, 30 to 35 minutes.

1	teaspoon extra-virgin olive oil
½	pound low-fat Italian turkey sausage links, casings removed
1	onion, chopped
1	(10-ounce) package frozen leaf spinach, thawed and squeezed dry
1	large egg, lightly beaten
8	(12 x 17-inch) sheets phyllo dough, thawed according to package directions

1. Preheat the oven to 375°F. Spray a baking sheet with nonstick spray; set aside.

2. Heat the oil in a large nonstick skillet over medium-high heat, then add the sausage and onion. Cook, breaking up the sausage with a wooden spoon, until browned and cooked through, about 10 minutes. Remove form the heat then stir in the spinach. Stir in the egg; mix well to combine.

3. Place 1 phyllo sheet on a work surface (cover the remaining phyllo with plastic wrap to retain moisture). Lightly spray the phyllo sheet with nonstick spray; top with a second sheet and lightly spray with nonstick spray. Fold the 2 sprayed sheets in half, making a 12 x 8 ½-inch rectangle. Spread one-fourth of the sausage mixture over the rectangle and roll up from one narrow end. Place seam-side down on the baking sheet and lightly spray with nonstick spray. Repeat with the remaining phyllo and filling, making a total of 4 rolls. Bake until golden brown, 20–25 minutes. Let cool 5 minutes before serving.

Per serving (1 roll): 156 Cal, 8 g Fat, 2 g Sat Fat, 0 g Trans Fat, 82 mg Chol, 644 mg Sod, 9 g Carb, 2 g Fib, 12 g Prot, 86 mg Calc. *POINTS* value: *3.*

Sausage and Spinach Rolls

3

LITE BITES

ESPECIALLY EASY AND
ALL WITH A *POINTS* VALUE OF 5 OR LESS

CARIBBEAN PORK ROLLS

MAKES 2 SERVINGS ♦

Skewered strips of apricot-glazed pork tenderloin and cool papaya salsa wrapped in crisp lettuce leaves make neat little packets for two or for twenty. The lettuce adds crunch without increasing the *POINTS* value and is a nice change from tortillas or pita bread. The salsa can be made up to a day ahead and refrigerated. Instead of using pork, try strips of grilled chicken, turkey, or even cooked brown rice.

½	cup finely diced papaya
¼	cup finely chopped red bell pepper
1	tablespoon finely chopped scallion
1	tablespoon chopped fresh cilantro
2	teaspoons honey
2	teaspoons fresh lime juice
¼	teaspoon crushed red pepper
⅛	teaspoon salt
1	tablespoon apricot preserves
1	tablespoon hoisin sauce
1	garlic clove, minced
1	teaspoon minced peeled fresh ginger
½	pound pork tenderloin, cut on diagonal into thin slices
4	large green leaf lettuce leaves

1. To make the salsa, combine the papaya, bell pepper, scallion, cilantro, honey, lime juice, crushed red pepper, and salt in a small bowl; set aside.

2. Line the broiler rack with foil; preheat the broiler.

3. Combine the apricot preserves, hoisin sauce, garlic, and ginger in another bowl. Add the pork; toss to coat. Thread the pork onto two 8-inch metal skewers. Place the skewers on the broiler rack. Broil 4 inches from the heat, turning occasionally, until the pork is browned, about 3 minutes on each side.

4. Place the lettuce on a work surface. Top each leaf with one-fourth of the pork and one-fourth of the salsa. Fold the two long sides of the lettuce over the filling. Starting from a short end, roll up the lettuce to enclose the filling. Repeat with the remaining lettuce, pork, and salsa, making a total of 4 rolls.

Per serving (2 rolls): 246 Cal, 5 g Fat, 2 g Sat Fat, 0 g Trans Fat, 72 mg Chol, 333 mg Sod, 23 g Carb, 2 g Fib, 27 g Prot, 42 mg Calc. *POINTS* **value: 5.**

Caribbean Pork Rolls

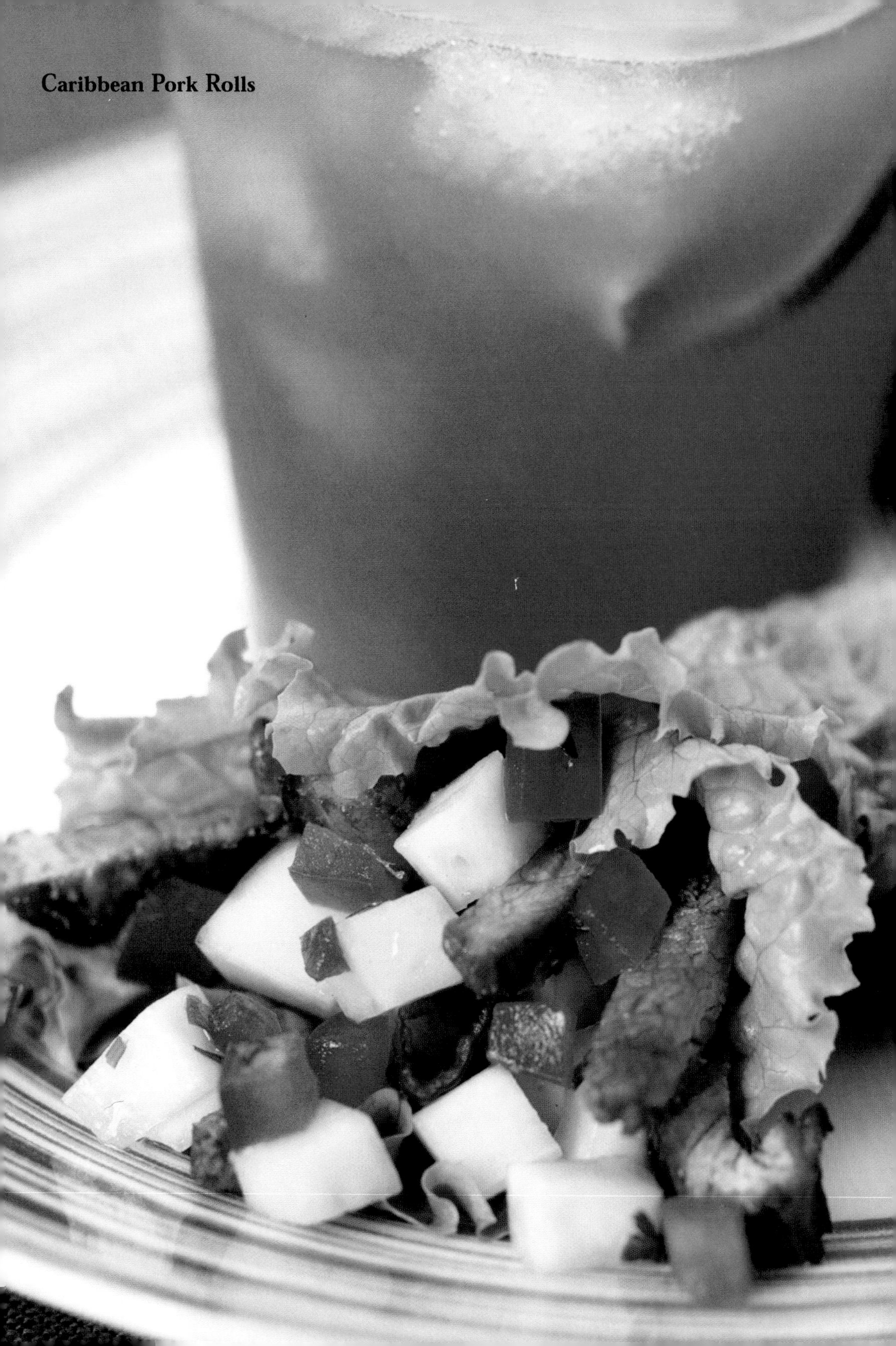

Coconut-Curry Chicken Nuggets

MAKES 4 SERVINGS

Chicken nuggets of any kind are always popular, and these are no exception. You can freeze the extra nuggets to enjoy another time. Simply place the coated nuggets on a small baking sheet in one layer. Cover with plastic wrap and freeze. Transfer the frozen nuggets to a zip-close plastic bag and store in the freezer for up to three months. No need to thaw before baking. Just allow an extra 5 minutes in the oven. For a strong curry flavor, use Madras curry powder.

½ cup mango chutney

1   teaspoon curry powder

½ teaspoon ground cumin

2   (6-ounce) skinless boneless chicken breasts, each cut into 8 pieces

½ cup sweetened flaked coconut, chopped

1. Preheat the oven to 425°F. Spray a baking sheet with nonstick spray.

2. Combine ¼ cup of the chutney, ½ teaspoon of the curry powder, and ¼ teaspoon of the cumin in a serving bowl; cover and refrigerate.

3. Combine the chicken, the remaining ¼ cup chutney, ½ teaspoon curry powder, and ¼ teaspoon cumin in a medium bowl; toss to coat. Put the coconut on a sheet of wax paper. Coat the chicken, one piece at a time, with the coconut.

4. Place the nuggets on the baking sheet. Bake until the chicken is cooked through and golden on the outside, about 15 minutes. Serve with the chutney sauce.

Per serving (4 nuggets): 196 Cal, 6 g Fat, 4 g Sat Fat, 0 g Trans Fat, 51 mg Chol, 91 mg Sod, 16 g Carb, 1 g Fib, 19 g Prot, 18 mg Calc. *POINTS* value: *4.*

TIP This recipe can easily be doubled for entertaining. Pile the nuggets on a platter and serve short bamboo picks alongside so they can be picked up with ease.

QUESADILLA CUBANO WITH CHIPOTLE MAYONNAISE

MAKES 2 SERVINGS ♦ ☕ ⏱

Two hot and trendy favorites in one: the Cuban sandwich (which is made with ham, turkey, or pork, plus cheese, and pickles) and the quesadilla (the Mexican version of a grilled cheese sandwich). The chipotle mayonnaise adds hot and smoky flavor. You may want to use more or fewer chipotles depending on your taste—or you may want to leave them out.

2   tablespoons fat-free mayonnaise

1   tablespoon sweet pickle relish

1   chipotle en adobo, chopped

2   (6-inch) fat-free flour tortillas

2   ounces thinly sliced turkey ham

2   tablespoons reduced-fat shredded Swiss cheese

1. Combine the mayonnaise, relish, and chipotle in a small bowl.

2. Spread the mayonnaise mixture over 1 tortilla, leaving a 1-inch border. Top with the ham and cheese, then cover with the remaining tortilla, pressing down gently.

3. Heat a large nonstick skillet over medium-high heat. Place the quesadilla in the skillet and cook, occasionally pressing down gently with a spatula, until crisp on the bottom, about 1½ minutes. Carefully turn the quesadilla and cook until it is crisp on the other side and the cheese is melted, about 1½ minutes longer. Transfer quesadilla to a plate and cut into 4 wedges. Serve at once.

Per serving (2 wedges): 168 Cal, 3 g Fat, 1 g Sat Fat, 0 g Trans Fat, 21 mg Chol, 992 mg Sod, 25 g Carb, 1 g Fib, 10 g Prot, 82 mg Calc. *POINTS* value: *3.*

———————————— ● ————————————

TIP   Chipotles in adobo sauce come in small cans and are found in the ethnic section of large supermarkets, in specialty food stores, and in Latin American markets.

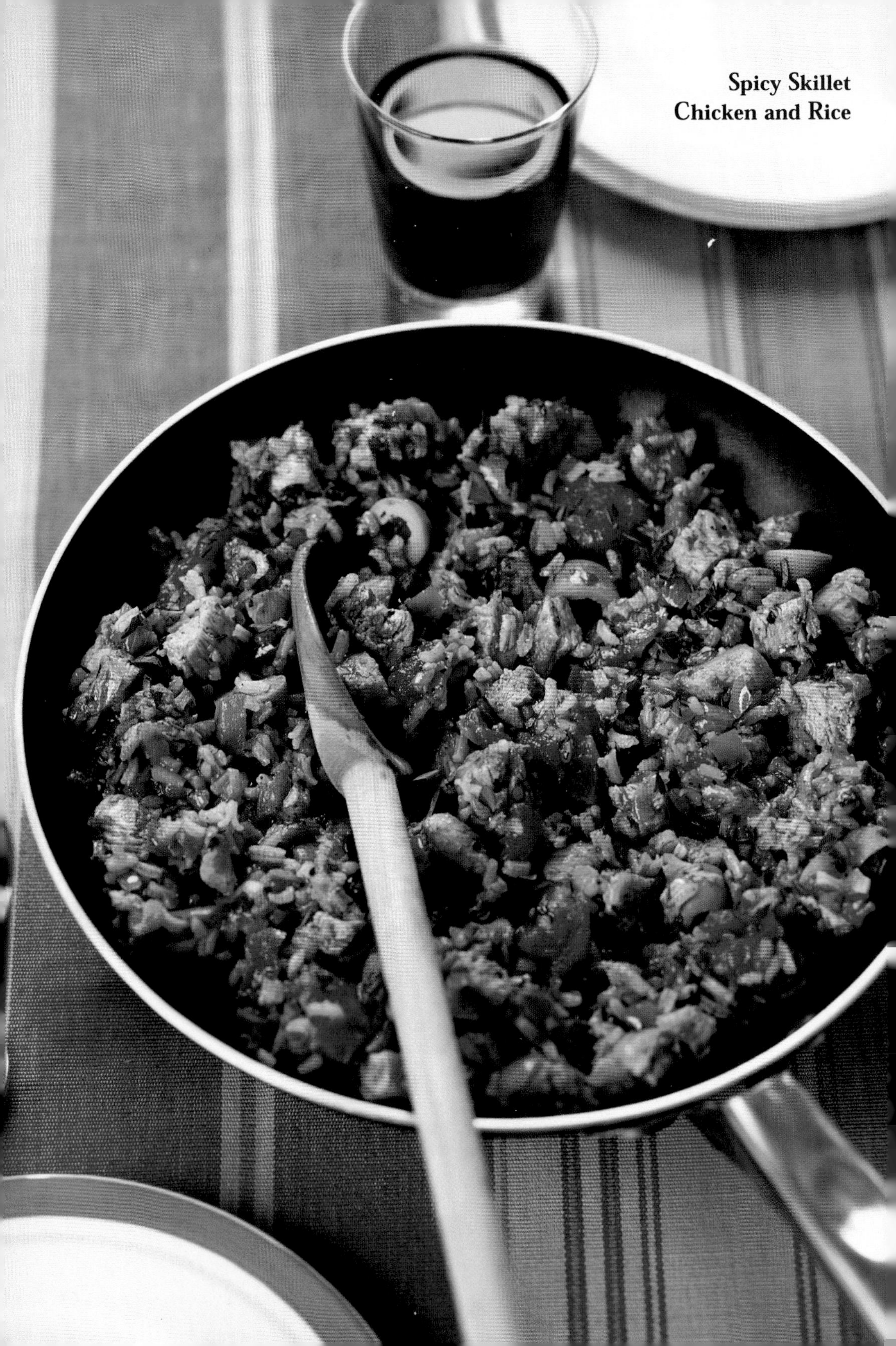

Spicy Skillet
Chicken and Rice

SPICY SKILLET CHICKEN AND RICE

MAKES 4 SERVINGS ♦ ☕ 🥫

This easy one-skillet meal is a great way to use leftover cooked chicken. You can refrigerate half of the meal to turn into a delicious main-dish salad the next day. Simply add a few pantry staples—½ cup rinsed and drained garbanzo beans (increase the per-serving *POINTS* value by 1), drained and sliced roasted red peppers (0 *POINTS* value), and drained canned artichoke hearts (1 cup increases the per-serving *POINTS* value by ½). Taste the salad. If the flavor needs to be perked up, add a squeeze of fresh lime juice and a generous pinch of Cajun seasoning.

1   teaspoon olive oil

1   onion, finely chopped

½   green bell pepper, seeded and chopped

1   garlic clove, minced

2   teaspoons Cajun seasoning

1   teaspoon chili powder

½   teaspoon ground cumin

⅓   cup long-grain white rice

1   (14½-ounce) can stewed tomatoes

½   cup water

1   cup cubed cooked chicken

4   pimiento-stuffed olives, halved

1. Heat the oil in a medium nonstick skillet over medium-high heat. Add the onion, bell pepper, and garlic and cook, stirring frequently, until softened, about 8 minutes. Add the Cajun seasoning, chili powder, and cumin; cook 1 minute. Add the rice and cook, stirring constantly, until the grains are coated, about 1 minute.
2. Add the tomatoes and water; bring to a boil. Reduce the heat and simmer, covered, 15 minutes. Add the chicken and olives; cook, covered, until the rice is tender and the chicken is heated through, about 5 minutes.

Per serving (⅔ cup): 190 Cal, 4 g Fat, 1 g Sat Fat, 0 g Trans Fat, 30 mg Chol, 682 mg Sod, 25 g Carb, 2 g Fib, 12 g Prot, 52 mg Calc. *POINTS* value: *4.*

TIP   Adding your own personal touch to recipes is easy when you have a well-stocked pantry. Canned tomatoes, sun-dried tomatoes, broths, wine, flavored vinegars, good-quality oils, chutney, mustard, olives, dried herbs, and capers all add dimension and flavor to food.

**Salmon Cakes with
Tarragon-Chive Sauce**

SALMON CAKES WITH TARRAGON-CHIVE SAUCE

MAKES 4 SERVINGS 🕐 🗑

This recipe is easily doubled for an elegant lunch gathering. You can even make the patties and the sauce ahead. They will keep, refrigerated, for up to two days and are delicious cold.

2 tablespoons cider vinegar

2 teaspoons Dijon mustard

2 teaspoons chopped fresh chives

1 teaspoon chopped fresh tarragon, or ¼ teaspoon dried

1 teaspoon capers, drained and chopped

1 teaspoon olive oil

¼ teaspoon freshly ground pepper

1 (14¾-ounce) can salmon, drained

¼ cup fat-free mayonnaise

¼ cup chopped scallions

3 tablespoons + ¼ cup plain dry bread crumbs

1 egg white, lightly beaten

1 cup mixed salad greens

8 grape tomatoes, halved

1. To make the sauce, combine the vinegar, mustard, chives, tarragon, capers, oil, and pepper in a small bowl. Cover and refrigerate until ready to serve.

2. Preheat the broiler. Spray a small baking sheet with nonstick spray.

3. To make the salmon cakes, with a fork, mash the salmon and bones in a large bowl. Add the mayonnaise, scallions, 3 tablespoons of the bread crumbs, and the egg white. With wet hands, shape the mixture into 4 patties.

4. Put the remaining ¼ cup bread crumbs on a sheet of wax paper. Coat the patties with the crumbs.

5. Place the patties on the baking sheet. Broil 4 inches from the heat until crisp and golden, about 4 minutes on each side. Refrigerate 2 of the patties for another day. Divide the greens and tomatoes between 2 plates. Top each plate with a salmon patty and drizzle a tablespoon of the sauce over each patty. Refrigerate the remaining sauce.

Per serving (1 patty, 1 tablespoon sauce, and ½ cup salad): 199 Cal, 7 g Fat, 2 g Sat Fat, 0 g Trans Fat, 46 mg Chol, 786 mg Sod, 14 g Carb, 1 g Fib, 20 g Prot, 222 mg Calc. *POINTS* value: *4.*

———————— ● ————————

TIP Did you know that a serving of canned salmon has more calcium than a glass of milk? The bones found in canned salmon are high in calcium and very soft, so we mash them into the patties (you'll never know they are there).

MEDITERRANEAN SALMON WRAPS

MAKES 2 SERVINGS ⊗ ⊕

These tasty wraps can also be prepared with leftover grilled salmon, tuna, or other cooked firm-fleshed fish (about ½ cup of small chunks) instead of canned salmon. For variety, instead of making a wrap, you can layer the salmon mixture with sliced tomato and onion on 2 slices of toasted whole-grain bread.

½   (7-ounce) can salmon, drained and flaked

5   oil-cured black olives, pitted and coarsely chopped

2   tablespoons fat-free mayonnaise

2   tablespoons finely chopped celery

1   tablespoon finely chopped red onion

1   tablespoon capers, drained and chopped

1   teaspoon Dijon mustard

2   (6-inch) fat-free flour tortillas

2   green leaf lettuce leaves

1. Combine the salmon, olives, mayonnaise, celery, onion, capers, and mustard in a small bowl.
2. Warm the tortillas according to package directions. Place a lettuce leaf on each tortilla and top with the salmon mixture. Roll up the tortillas and cut diagonally in half.

Per serving (2 halves): 167 Cal, 4 g Fat, 1 g Sat Fat, 0 g Trans Fat, 22 mg Chol, 870 mg Sod, 22 g Carb, 1 g Fib, 11 g Prot, 133 mg Calc. *POINTS* value: *3.*

TUNA TOSTADAS

MAKES 2 SERVINGS

Rather than offering the more usual tostada topping of a tomato-based salsa, here is a refreshing vinegar-spiked herb sauce otherwise known as chimichurri in Argentina, where it is a common table condiment served alongside grilled meat. Make a generous batch and store, refrigerated, for up to five days. Serve it with grilled chicken or fish or as a topping for green beans or cauliflower.

1	tablespoon chopped fresh parsley
1	tablespoon chopped fresh cilantro
1	tablespoon minced red onion
1	garlic clove, minced
1	teaspoon cider vinegar
1	(6-ounce) tuna fillet
¼	teaspoon salt
¼	teaspoon freshly ground pepper
½	teaspoon olive oil
2	(6-inch) corn tortillas
2	teaspoons toasted pine nuts

Fresh cilantro sprigs (optional)

1. To make the herb sauce, combine the parsley, chopped cilantro, onion, garlic, and vinegar in a small bowl; set aside.

2. Sprinkle the tuna with the salt and pepper. Heat the oil in a small nonstick skillet over medium heat. Add the tuna and cook, turning once, until browned on the outside but slightly pink in the center, about 5 minutes. Transfer the tuna to a plate; let rest 5 minutes.

3. Wipe the skillet clean. Spray with nonstick spray and set over medium heat. Add 1 tortilla to the skillet and cook until crisp and golden, 2–3 minutes on each side. Transfer to a plate. Repeat with the second tortilla.

4. Cut the tuna into ¼-inch-thick slices. Place the tuna on the tortillas, top with the sauce, and sprinkle with pine nuts. Top with cilantro sprigs (if using) and serve at once.

Per serving (1 tostada with 2 tablespoons salsa and 1 teaspoon nuts): 198 Cal, 8 g Fat, 2 g Sat Fat, 0 g Trans Fat, 50 mg Chol, 384 mg Sod, 14 g Carb, 2 g Fib, 19 g Prot, 63 mg Calc. *POINTS* value: *4*.

TIP A mini food processor is a great time-saver. They are inexpensive, take up very little counter space, and perform a variety of functions quickly and efficiently. It makes quick work of preparing the salsa.

SHRIMP-COCKTAIL KEBABS WITH LIME VINAIGRETTE

MAKES 2 SERVINGS 🍲 🕐

Bursting with flavor, this shrimp cocktail makes an impressive first course that can easily be doubled or even tripled. You can leave the tails on the shrimp for a pretty presentation. And, if you like, use tropical fruit in place of the avocado: mango, papaya, or chunks of fresh pineapple would all be delicious. We suggest using glasses for serving the kebabs, but margarita glasses will also work well.

8   large shrimp, peeled and deveined

1   tablespoon fresh lime juice

2   teaspoons honey

1   teaspoon extra-virgin olive oil

1   teaspoon cider vinegar

1   teaspoon coarse-grained Dijon mustard

1   teaspoon chopped fresh cilantro

⅛   teaspoon crushed red pepper

½   avocado, peeled and cut into 8 chunks

4   cherry tomatoes, halved

1½ cups mixed baby salad greens

2   tablespoons finely chopped red onion

1. Bring a medium saucepan of water to a boil; add the shrimp. Reduce the heat and simmer until the shrimp are just opaque in the center, 3–4 minutes. Drain and rinse under cold running water to stop the cooking. Pat the shrimp dry with paper towels.

2. Stir together the lime juice, honey, oil, vinegar, mustard, cilantro, and crushed red pepper in a bowl until blended. Stir in the shrimp, avocado, and tomatoes; gently toss to coat.

3. Alternately thread the shrimp, avocado, and tomatoes on 4 (6-inch) wooden skewers; reserve any vinaigrette remaining in the bowl. Divide the greens between 2 glasses; place 2 kebabs in each glass. Sprinkle with the onion and drizzle with the reserved vinaigrette.

Per serving (2 kebabs with 2 tablespoons vinaigrette): 157 Cal, 10 g Fat, 1 g Sat Fat, 0 g Trans Fat, 47 mg Chol, 136 mg Sod, 14 g Carb, 4 g Fib, 7 g Prot, 41 mg Calc. *POINTS* value: *3.*

---●---

TIP Make this a no-cook recipe by purchasing already cooked peeled deveined shrimp. For entertaining, purchase decorative party picks for skewering the shrimp.

Shrimp-Cocktail Kebabs with Lime Vinaigrette

MARISCADA VERDE

MAKES 2 SERVINGS 🍲

Mariscada is a magnificent Brazilian shellfish stew that usually contains white wine, broth, ripe tomatoes, and fresh herbs. A wide variety of seafood can be used—scallops, crabmeat, and hunks of red snapper, cod, or monkfish are all good choices. If you really feel like indulging, add some lobster. Be sure to serve the stew with crusty bread (up your *POINTS* value by 1 with a 1-ounce chunk) for sopping up the flavorful juices.

2	teaspoons olive oil
½	pound mussels, scrubbed and debearded
8	littleneck clams, scrubbed
6	large shrimp, peeled and deveined
2	plum tomatoes, diced
2	garlic cloves, minced
½	cup reduced-sodium chicken broth
¼	cup dry white wine
¼	cup chopped fresh basil
1	tablespoon chopped fresh parsley
1	tablespoon chopped fresh tarragon
1	tablespoon chopped fresh cilantro

1. Heat the oil in a large nonstick skillet over medium-high heat. Add the mussels and clams. Cover and cook until the mussels begin to open, about 4 minutes; transfer them to a large bowl as they open.
2. Cover the skillet and cook until the clams begin to open, about 3 minutes longer; add them to the mussels in the bowl as they open. Discard any mussels or clams that do not open.
3. Add the shrimp to the skillet and cook, stirring occasionally, until just opaque in the center, about 3 minutes. Add the shrimp to the mussels and clams.
4. Add the tomatoes and garlic to the skillet. Cook over medium heat, stirring occasionally, until the tomatoes begin to soften, about 5 minutes. Stir in the broth, wine, basil, parsley, tarragon, and cilantro. Return the seafood to the skillet and cook until just heated through, about 2 minutes.

Per serving (1¾ cups): 139 Cal, 6 g Fat, 1 g Sat Fat, 0 g Trans Fat, 58 mg Chol, 177 mg Sod, 7 g Carb, 1 g Fib, 14 g Prot, 68 mg Calc. *POINTS* value: *3.*

———————————●———————————

TIP Clams can be gritty and sandy, so you'll need to rinse them several times in cold water. Discard any raw clams that don't close when gently tapped.

Mariscada Verde

Pepperoni and Pimiento-Stuffed Clams

MAKES 2 SERVINGS

Using fresh bread crumbs rather than store-bought dry bread crumbs really makes a difference here. Choose a firm-textured white bread, preferably a day or two old. If the bread you have on hand is too fresh and soft, let it stand, uncovered, at room temperature, for about 30 minutes until it has a chance to dry out a bit. This will make it easier to get good crumbs.

2   teaspoons olive oil

1   shallot, minced (2 tablespoons)

2   slices turkey pepperoni, finely chopped (1 tablespoon)

2   teaspoons finely chopped pimientos

1   garlic clove, minced

2   slices firm white bread, made into fine crumbs

1   tablespoon finely chopped fresh parsley

1   teaspoon grated lemon zest

1   dozen littleneck clams, scrubbed and shucked (12 half-shells reserved)

1. Heat the oil in a medium nonstick skillet over medium-low heat. Add the shallot, pepperoni, pimientos, and garlic. Cook, stirring constantly, until the shallot begins to soften, about 2 minutes. Remove from the heat and stir in the bread crumbs, parsley, and lemon zest.

2. Preheat the broiler. Place a clam in each reserved half-shell and top with the crumb mixture.

3. Place the stuffed clams in a broiler pan or jelly-roll pan. Lightly spray the clams with nonstick spray. Broil 4 inches from the heat until the crumbs are golden and the clams are just cooked through, 8–9 minutes. Serve at once.

Per serving (6 clams): 172 Cal, 8 g Fat, 0 g Sat Fat, 0 g Trans Fat, 22 mg Chol, 236 mg Sod, 16 g Carb, 0 g Fib, 10 g Prot, 66 mg Calc. *POINTS* value: *4.*

TIP A microplane grater does a wonderful job of removing the flavorful yellow part of the lemon peel without grating any of the bitter white pith that is underneath. The grater is available in cookware stores and some large supermarkets.

Spinach-Stuffed Mushrooms with Pine Nuts and Prosciutto

MAKES 2 SERVINGS

Portobello mushrooms stuffed with savory spinach make a great lite bite, first course, or side dish for grilled chicken, fish, or pork. Portobellos can vary in size. Here you need them about 4 inches in diameter. Choose mushrooms that are heavy for their size, firm, and almost moist looking. Avoid any that are dry or wrinkled. If you purchase them ahead, place them in a container, cover with a folded up paper towel, and top with the container cover. The paper towel will absorb any moisture.

1   teaspoon olive oil

1   garlic clove, minced

½   (5-ounce) bag baby spinach leaves (about 3 cups)

¼   cup water

2   tablespoons plain dry bread crumbs

1   ounce prosciutto, finely chopped

1   tablespoon pine nuts

2   portobello mushrooms (about ¼ pound), stems discarded, caps wiped clean

1. Preheat the oven to 425°F. Spray a 7 x 11-inch baking dish with nonstick spray.

2. Heat the oil in a medium nonstick skillet over medium heat. Add the garlic and cook, stirring constantly, until fragrant and light golden, about 1 minute. Add the spinach and 2 tablespoons of the water. Cook, stirring occasionally, until the spinach begins to wilt, about 2 minutes. Remove from the heat. Stir in the bread crumbs, prosciutto, and pine nuts.

3. Place the mushroom caps in the baking dish. Fill the mushroom cavities with the spinach mixture, mounding it slightly. Add the remaining 2 tablespoons water to the baking dish. Bake until the mushrooms are tender and the filling is hot, about 25 minutes.

Per serving (1 mushroom): 116 Cal, 6 g Fat, 1 g Sat Fat, 0 g Trans Fat, 7 mg Chol, 270 mg Sod, 10 g Carb, 2 g Fib, 7 g Prot, 59 mg Calc. *POINTS* value: *2.*

———————— • ————————

TIP The small amount of prosciutto adds full, rich flavor to this dish. For best flavor, choose prosciutto imported from Italy such as prosciutto di Parma, also called Parma ham.

THAI SPRING ROLLS

MAKES 2 SERVINGS ♦ ⊗ ✦

These delicate bite-size rolls are easy to make and require no cooking: The rice paper wrappers and noodles are simply softened in warm water. Rice-paper wrappers are thin, semi-transparent disks. They are sold in large supermarkets and in Asian stores. Spring rolls lend themselves to endless variations: You can add 2 ounces of shredded cooked chicken breast to the filling and increase the per-serving *POINTS* value by 1. For added color and crunch, toss in some finely shredded red cabbage, thinly sliced cucumber strips, watercress sprigs, or fresh mint leaves.

2	tablespoons reduced-sodium soy sauce
2	teaspoons seasoned rice vinegar
2	teaspoons honey
1	teaspoon chili garlic sauce
½	teaspoon Asian (dark) sesame oil
1	ounce thin rice noodles
1	small carrot, shredded
1	large green leaf lettuce leaf, shredded
1	scallion, thinly sliced
1	tablespoon chopped fresh cilantro
4	(6-inch) rice-paper wrappers

1. Wisk together the soy sauce, vinegar, honey, chili garlic sauce, and sesame oil in a large bowl; set aside.
2. Place the rice noodles in another large bowl and add enough hot water to cover; let stand until the noodles soften, about 10 minutes. Drain; rinse under cold running water and drain again. Cut the noodles into 2-inch lengths and add to the soy mixture in the bowl. Add the carrot, lettuce, scallion, and cilantro to the bowl; toss to mix.
3. To assemble the rolls, dip one rice-paper wrapper at a time in a bowl of warm water until softened, about 45 seconds; transfer to a clean kitchen towel. Place one-fourth of the noodle mixture in the center of each wrapper. Fold in two opposite sides, then roll up to enclose the filling. Cut each roll diagonally in half.

Per serving (2 rolls): 157 Cal, 2 g Fat, 0 g Sat Fat, 0 g Trans Fat, 8 mg Chol, 596 mg Sod, 33 g Carb, 2 g Fib, 3 g Prot, 25 mg Calc. *POINTS* value: *3.*

———————●———————

TIP You can make the spring rolls ahead of time. Cover with damp paper towels and plastic wrap to prevent them from drying out, then refrigerate until ready to serve.

CRISPY VEGETABLE FRITTERS

MAKES 2 SERVINGS

Fritters are at their crispiest when fresh out of the skillet, but you can prepare them several hours ahead and set aside on a double layer of paper towels. When ready to serve, transfer the fritters to a foil-lined baking sheet (for easy cleanup) and reheat in a 400°F oven until heated through, 6 to 8 minutes. They are delicious unadorned but a spoonful of chunky, unsweetened applesauce adds a tart-sweet contrast.

1   (4-ounce) red potato, peeled
1   small zucchini
1   small carrot, coarsely grated
1   scallion, finely chopped
1   egg white, lightly beaten
1   tablespoon all-purpose flour
$\frac{1}{2}$ teaspoon salt
$\frac{1}{4}$ teaspoon pepper
1   tablespoon canola oil

1. Put the potato in a saucepan with boiling water to cover. Cook about 6 minutes; drain. Cover with cold water to cool.

2. Meanwhile, coarsely grate the zucchini onto a double layer of paper towels; spread the zucchini out and let stand 3 minutes to drain. Combine the zucchini with the carrot, scallion, egg white, flour, salt, and pepper in a large bowl. Drain the potato, pat dry, then coarsely grate over the zucchini mixture.

3. Heat the oil on a large nonstick griddle or in a large nonstick skillet. Drop the batter onto the griddle by $\frac{1}{4}$-cup measures, making a total of 6 fritters. Cook until golden, about 3 minutes on each side.

Per serving (3 fritters): 149 Cal, 7 g Fat, 0 g Sat Fat, 0 g Trans Fat, 0 mg Chol, 631 mg Sod, 18 g Carb, 3 g Fib, 4 g Prot, 28 mg Calc. *POINTS* value: *3*.

———————————— ● ————————————

TIP To serve these fritters as hors d'oeuvres, cook up heaping tablespoon measures of the batter, making about 18 small fritters. Arrange them on a serving tray and top each fritter with a little sour cream and a sprinkling of snipped fresh chives.

Crunchy Peanut Noodles

CRUNCHY PEANUT NOODLES

MAKES 4 SERVINGS 🌢 ☕ 🌿

This lively and refreshing salad gets its crunch from cucumbers, snow peas, and bell peppers. Leftovers keep well, stored in a covered container, in the refrigerator for up to two days and make a great packed lunch. For best flavor, let the noodles stand at room temperature for about 15 minutes before serving.

3 tablespoons reduced-fat smooth peanut butter

2 tablespoons seasoned rice vinegar

1 tablespoon reduced-sodium soy sauce

1 tablespoon water

1 teaspoon Asian (dark) sesame oil

1 teaspoon sugar

¼ teaspoon crushed red pepper

4 ounces thin linguine

½ red bell pepper, seeded and cut into thin strips

¼ cup fresh snow peas, trimmed and cut on diagonal in half

¼ small cucumber, peeled, seeded, and diced

2 scallions, finely chopped

2 tablespoons chopped cilantro

2 tablespoons chopped dry-roasted peanuts

1. Whisk together the peanut butter, vinegar, soy sauce, water, sesame oil, sugar, and crushed red pepper in a small bowl until smooth and creamy; set aside.

2. Meanwhile, cook the linguine according to package directions. Drain; rinse under cold running water and drain again.

3. Combine the linguine, peanut sauce, bell pepper, snow peas, cucumber, scallions, and cilantro in a serving bowl. Toss gently to mix. Sprinkle with the peanuts before serving.

Per serving (⅔ cup): 235 Cal, 8 g Fat, 2 g Sat Fat, 0 g Trans Fat, 0 mg Chol, 357 mg Sod, 33 g Carb, 2 g Fib, 8 g Prot, 29 mg Calc. *POINTS* value: *5.*

WALDORF PASTA SALAD WITH CREAMY CITRUS DRESSING

MAKES 4 SERVINGS

This classic salad is the perfect side dish for picnics and barbecues because it goes so well with chicken, turkey, pork, and fish. It was created by the maître d'hôtel of the Waldorf-Astoria Hotel in 1893 and contained just three ingredients: apples, celery, and mayonnaise. Later grapes and nuts were added, and it has been popular ever since. You can store leftovers of the salad in a covered container in the refrigerator for up to two days.

1   cup rotini pasta

1   apple, cored and cut into
    ½-inch chunks

½   cup seedless grapes, halved

1   small carrot, chopped

1   celery stalk, finely chopped

2   tablespoons raisins

2   tablespoons chopped
    fresh parsley

¼   cup fat-free mayonnaise

1   tablespoon fresh lemon juice

1   tablespoon orange juice

2   teaspoons honey

½   teaspoon salt

2   tablespoons toasted
    chopped walnuts

1. Cook the pasta according to package directions. Drain; rinse under cold running water and drain again. Transfer the pasta to a serving bowl. Add apple, grapes, carrot, celery, raisins, and parsley; toss to combine.

2. Whisk together the mayonnaise, lemon juice, orange juice, honey, and salt in a small bowl until well blended. Add the dressing to the pasta mixture; toss gently to coat. Sprinkle with the walnuts and serve.

Per serving (about ¾ cup): 216 Cal, 3 g Fat, 0 g Sat Fat, 0 g Trans Fat, 0 mg Chol, 545 mg Sod, 43 g Carb, 3 g Fib, 5 g Prot, 28 mg Calc. *POINTS* value: *4*.

———— ● ————

TIP You don't have to toast the walnuts, but toasting crisps them and brings out their flavor. The easiest way to toast nuts is to put them in a skillet and cook over medium heat, tossing occasionally, until their edges turn brown. Transfer the nuts to a plate to cool so they don't continue to cook.

Waldorf Pasta Salad with
Creamy Citrus Dressing

VIDALIA ONION TART

MAKES 2 SERVINGS

These delectably sweet and juicy pale yellow onions are available for a short time only—from May through June. Store onions in a cool, dark place or in the refrigerator and be sure to allow for good air circulation. If you can't find Vidalia onions, Texas Sweets and Walla Wallas are good alternatives.

½ teaspoon olive oil

1 large (about ¾ pound) Vidalia onion, thinly sliced

¼ cup water

¼ teaspoon salt

4 kalamata olives, pitted and chopped

1 teaspoon chopped fresh thyme

¼ teaspoon freshly ground pepper

2 (12 x 17-inch) sheets phyllo dough, at room temperature

2 tablespoons shredded Jarlsberg cheese

1. Heat the oil in a medium nonstick skillet over medium-high heat. Add the onion, water, and salt; bring to a boil. Reduce the heat and simmer, covered, stirring occasionally, until the onion is very soft, about 20 minutes. Remove from the heat and stir in the olives, thyme, and pepper; cool slightly.

2. Preheat the oven to 400°F.

3. Place 1 phyllo sheet on a dry work surface; lightly spray with nonstick spray. As you work, keep the sheets of phyllo covered to keep them from drying out. Top with a second phyllo sheet; lightly spray with nonstick spray. Cut into 4 rectangles. Place the rectangles on top of each other to form a stack. Roll the edges of the phyllo in to make a small rimmed edge; place on a baking sheet.

4. Spread the onion mixture evenly over the phyllo. Bake the tart until the edges are golden brown, about 20 minutes. Sprinkle the tart with the cheese and bake until the cheese melts, about 5 minutes longer.

Per serving (½ tart): 182 Cal, 5 g Fat, 2 g Sat Fat, 0 g Trans Fat, 6 mg Chol, 471 mg Sod, 30 g Carb, 4 g Fib, 6 g Prot, 109 mg Calc. *POINTS* value: *3.*

Vidalia Onion Tart

EGGPLANT ROLLS WITH RED PEPPER PESTO

MAKES 4 SERVINGS

Our tasty pesto is made with jarred roasted red peppers for ease of preparation. But, if your home garden produces summer peppers, be sure to use them here (see our Tip, below). You can save four of these eggplant rolls and half of the pesto to serve another day. Simply refrigerate them for up to three days and bring to room temperature before serving.

½   cup jarred roasted red peppers, drained

2   tablespoons chopped fresh basil

1   garlic clove, minced

2   teaspoons balsamic vinegar

¼   teaspoon salt

1   (½-pound) eggplant, cut lengthwise into 8 slices

1½ cups fat-free ricotta cheese

¼   cup grated Parmesan cheese

2   ounces thinly sliced prosciutto, finely chopped

2   teaspoons chopped fresh rosemary

¼   teaspoon nutmeg

¼   teaspoon freshly ground pepper

8   fresh basil leaves

1. To make the pesto, puree the peppers, chopped basil, garlic, vinegar, and salt in a food processor or blender. Transfer the pesto to a small bowl.

2. Preheat the broiler. Spray a baking sheet with nonstick spray. Arrange the eggplant on the baking sheet in one layer and lightly spray with nonstick spray. Broil 4 inches from the heat until browned, about 3 minutes on each side.

3. Combine the ricotta cheese, Parmesan, prosciutto, rosemary, nutmeg, and pepper in a medium bowl.

4. To assemble the rolls, place a basil leaf at one end of each eggplant slice and top with about 3 tablespoons of the ricotta mixture. Beginning at the filled end, roll up the eggplant slices and place, seam-side down, on a serving plate. Serve with the pesto.

Per serving (2 rolls with 2 tablespoons pesto): 151 Cal, 4 g Fat, 2 g Sat Fat, 0 g Trans Fat, 20 mg Chol, 460 mg Sod, 11 g Carb, 2 g Fib, 18 g Prot, 243 mg Calc. *POINTS* value: *3*.

TIP To grill bell peppers, cut 1 or 2 peppers lengthwise in half and grill or broil until nicely charred. Pop them into a zip-close plastic bag to steam for 20 minutes, then slip off the skins and remove the stems and seeds. Store any unused peppers in a covered container in the refrigerator for up to four days.

GARLICKY SPINACH AND GOAT CHEESE PIZZA

MAKES 4 SERVINGS 🍲 🕐 🥕

The two extra servings of this pizza make a great addition to lunch boxes. Wrap and refrigerate the leftover pizza wedges for up to three days. They're great cold, but if you get a chance, you can warm them in a toaster-oven for a few minutes.

1   teaspoon olive oil

2   garlic cloves, minced

½   (6-ounce) bag baby spinach leaves (about 3 cups)

¼   teaspoon salt

¼   teaspoon freshly ground pepper

1   (5-ounce) prebaked thin pizza crust

1   plum tomato, chopped

2   ounces goat cheese

1   tablespoon chopped fresh oregano, or 1 teaspoon dried

1. Preheat the oven to 450°F.

2. Heat the oil in a small nonstick skillet over medium-high heat. Add the garlic and cook until golden, about 1 minute. Add the spinach, salt, and pepper. Cook, stirring occasionally, until the spinach begins to wilt, about 2 minutes. Remove from the heat and spread over the pizza crust. Sprinkle with the tomato, goat cheese, and oregano.

3. Bake until the topping is hot and the cheese just begins to melt, about 10 minutes. Cool slightly and cut into 4 wedges.

Per serving (¼ of pizza): 156 Cal, 7 g Fat, 3 g Sat Fat, 0 g Trans Fat, 11 mg Chol, 397 mg Sod, 18 g Carb, 2 g Fib, 7 g Prot, 49 mg Calc. *POINTS* value: *3*.

Pita with Tomatoes, Olives, and Parmesan

MAKES 2 SERVINGS ✖ 🕒 ➶

All the flavors of summer come together in this simple open-face pita sandwich. You can add thin strips of red and green bell peppers or halved yellow pear tomatoes without increasing your *POINTS* value. Be sure to wash the arugula thoroughly as it can be quite sandy. Or buy bagged cleaned arugula. If you like, watercress or mixed baby greens or a combination of the two, can be used in place of the arugula.

½ cup fat-free ricotta cheese

1 tablespoon prepared pesto

¼ teaspoon freshly ground pepper

1 (6-inch) whole-wheat pita bread, split and toasted

¼ cup baby arugula leaves

4 grape tomatoes, quartered

4 kalamata olives, pitted and coarsely chopped

½ teaspoon extra-virgin olive oil

½ ounce piece Parmesan cheese, made into shavings (see Tip)

1. Combine the ricotta cheese, pesto, and pepper in a small bowl.

2. Spread the ricotta mixture onto both pita halves. Top evenly with the arugula, tomatoes, and olives. Drizzle with the oil, then top with the Parmesan cheese. Serve at once.

Per serving (1 piece): 218 Cal, 9 g Fat, 2 g Sat Fat, 0 g Trans Fat, 12 mg Chol, 446 mg Sod, 22 g Carb, 3 g Fib, 14 g Prot, 231 mg Calc. *POINTS* value: *5*.

———————●———————

TIP Fresh Parmesan shavings are easy to make. Starting with a wedge of Parmesan cheese and using a vegetable peeler, in a downward motion, shave off thin strips from the wedge (one-half ounce makes about 2 tablespoons shavings). For best flavor, seek out authentic Parmigiano-Reggiano cheese.

TOMATO-CHUTNEY CROSTINI

MAKES 2 SERVINGS

You'll be using only half of this tasty chutney in this recipe; save the remaining half to serve another day. It will keep in the refrigerator for up to one week. You might try the chutney on Melba toast rounds for a quick snack. Or serve it as a tasty topping for grilled chicken, roast pork tenderloin, or turkey burgers.

2	teaspoons olive oil
1/4	cup finely chopped onion
1/4	cup diced green bell pepper
2	plum tomatoes, diced
3	tablespoons packed light brown sugar
3	tablespoons cider vinegar
1/2	teaspoon salt
1/4	teaspoon ground allspice
2	tablespoons pine nuts
1	tablespoon chopped fresh parsley
1/4	(8-ounce) baguette, cut into 4 slices and toasted

1. To make the chutney, heat the oil in a small nonstick saucepan over medium-high heat. Add the onion and bell pepper. Cook, stirring occasionally, until softened, about 8 minutes. Add the tomatoes, brown sugar, vinegar, salt, and allspice; bring to a boil. Reduce the heat and simmer, covered, stirring occasionally, until the flavors blend and the chutney has thickened, about 20 minutes. Remove from the heat; stir in the pine nuts and parsley.

2. Spoon about 2 tablespoons of the chutney onto each piece of toast. Serve at once.

Per serving (2 crostini): 173 Cal, 6 g Fat, 1 g Sat Fat, 0 g Trans Fat, 0 mg Chol, 468 mg Sod, 28 g Carb, 2 g Fib, 4 g Prot, 39 mg Calc. *POINTS* value: *4*.

4

Two Meals from One

Ten Basic Recipes and
Ten Easy Spin-offs

SIZZLING STEAK AND ONION WITH HASH BROWNS

MAKES 2 SERVINGS (PLUS LEFTOVER STEAK) ♦

There's no need to peel the potato for the hash browns here. In fact, potato skins are a good source of fiber, iron, potassium, phosphorous, calcium, zinc, and vitamin B. Steamed sugar snap peas make a crunchy accompaniment to this dish.

1   (1-pound) boneless sirloin steak, trimmed of all visible fat

2   teaspoons Cajun seasoning

1   medium onion, cut crosswise into 4 slices

2   teaspoons olive oil

1   garlic clove, minced

1   (10-ounce) potato, scrubbed and shredded

¼   teaspoon salt

1. Spray broiler rack with nonstick spray; preheat broiler.

2. Sprinkle both sides of steak with the Cajun seasoning; place on broiler rack. Arrange onion slices around steak; spray onion lightly with nonstick spray. Broil steak and onion 5 inches from the heat until an instant-read thermometer inserted in center of the steak registers 145°F for medium-rare, 5–6 minutes on each side and onion is lightly browned, 3–4 minutes on each side.

3. Meanwhile, heat the oil in a medium nonstick skillet over medium heat. Add the garlic and cook, stirring frequently, until fragrant, about 30 seconds. Add the potato and salt, stirring to incorporate the garlic then press down into a flat cake in the skillet. Cover the skillet and cook until golden on the bottom, about 5 minutes. With a nonstick spatula, cut the potato cake into fourths, then turn and cook, covered, until golden on the other side, about 5 minutes longer.

4. Transfer steak to a cutting board, let stand 5 minutes; cut in half. Refrigerate half of steak for up to 3 days for later use.

5. Cut the remaining steak, against the grain and on a diagonal, into 8–10 slices. Serve the steak with the onion slices and hash brown cakes.

Per serving (4–5 steak slices, 2 onion slices, and 2 hash brown cakes): 320 Cal, 9 g Fat, 2 g Sat Fat, 0 g Trans Fat, 60 mg Chol, 611 mg Sod, 34 g Carb, 4 g Fib, 26 g Prot, 31 mg Calc. *POINTS* value: *6.*

**Sizzling Steak and Onion
with Hash Browns**

Beef, Pepper, and Mushroom Burrito with Guacamole

MAKES 2 SERVINGS

This is a simple way to serve leftover steak, chicken, turkey, or pork. If you prefer your very own fajita-style wrap (and for no change in *POINTS* value), you can spoon the filling into 2 (6-inch) fat-free flour tortillas. Serve any filling that will not stuff into the tortillas on the side. For stronger mushroom flavor, consider using fresh shiitake mushrooms (remember to discard their tough stems) instead of white mushrooms.

½ pound reserved cooked steak from Sizzling Steak and Onion with Hash Browns (page 86)

1 teaspoon olive oil

1 onion, halved lengthwise, then sliced crosswise

1 red bell pepper, seeded and cut into ¼-inch-wide strips

¼ pound fresh white mushrooms, sliced

⅓ cup jarred taco sauce

2 tablespoons chopped fresh cilantro or parsley

1 burrito-size (10-inch) fat-free flour tortilla, warmed

¼ cup prepared guacamole or fat-free sour cream

1. Cut the steak into thin strips against the grain and on a diagonal; set aside.

2. Heat the oil in a large nonstick skillet over medium heat. Add the onion, bell pepper, and mushrooms. Cook, stirring frequently, until softened and lightly browned, about 8 minutes. Stir in the sliced steak, taco sauce, and cilantro. Cook, uncovered, stirring occasionally, until heated through, about 3 minutes.

3. Spoon the steak-and-vegetable mixture onto the tortilla, then top with the guacamole. Roll up and cut in half on a slight diagonal.

Per serving (½ burrito): 375 Cal, 10 g Fat, 2 g Sat Fat, 0 g Trans Fat, 60 mg Chol, 1010 mg Sod, 41 g Carb, 6 g Fib, 30 g Prot, 83 mg Calc. *POINTS* value: *8.*

———————————————•———————————————

TIP To lower the per-serving *POINTS* value by 1, omit the guacamole or sour cream and use ½ cup chopped tomato and ¼ cup chopped scallions instead.

Beef, Pepper, and Mushroom Burrito with Guacamole

BEEF, BEER, AND VEGETABLE STEW

MAKES 2 SERVINGS (PLUS LEFTOVER STEW)

Dark beer adds rich color and flavor to this comforting stew, which, like many stews, lends itself well to double-batch cooking. You can either refrigerate or freeze the extra stew for another day and simply serve it again, or transform it into our comforting Beef and Noodle Bake (page 91). If you like, serve with a 1-ounce slice of crusty peasant bread and up the *POINTS* value by 2.

1   pound beef top round, trimmed of all visible fat and cut into ³/₄-inch chunks

2   tablespoons all-purpose flour

1   teaspoon paprika

¹/₂ teaspoon salt

¹/₄ teaspoon freshly ground pepper

2   teaspoons canola oil

1   large onion, chopped

2   garlic cloves, minced

1   cup reduced-sodium beef broth

³/₄ cup dark beer, such as stout or Guinness

5   carrots, cut into ¹/₂-inch pieces

1   parsnip, peeled and cut into ¹/₂-inch pieces

¹/₂ pound fresh green beans, trimmed and halved

1¹/₂ teaspoons chopped fresh thyme, or ¹/₂ teaspoon dried

1. Put the beef, flour, paprika, salt, and pepper in a zip-close plastic bag. Shake the bag until the beef is evenly coated with the flour mixture.

2. Heat 1 teaspoon of the oil in a nonstick Dutch oven over medium-high heat. Add half of the beef and cook until browned on all sides, about 5 minutes. Transfer the beef to a plate. Repeat with the remaining 1 teaspoon oil and the beef.

3. Add the onion and garlic to the pot. Cook, stirring frequently and scraping up the browned bits with a wooden spoon, until softened, about 5 minutes. Return the beef to the pot.

4. Stir in the broth, beer, carrots, and parsnip; bring to a boil. Reduce the heat and simmer, covered, about 1 hour. Stir in the green beans. Simmer, covered, until the beef and vegetables are fork-tender, about 15 minutes longer.

5. Spoon half of the stew (about 2¹/₂ cups) into a container and refrigerate, covered, for up to 3 days for later use. Stir the thyme into the remaining stew and simmer 2 minutes.

Per serving (1¹/₄ cups): 272 Cal, 6 g Fat, 2 g Sat Fat, 0 g Trans Fat, 60 mg Chol, 416 mg Sod, 25 g Carb, 6 g Fib, 26 g Prot, 76 mg Calc. *POINTS* value: *5.*

BEEF AND NOODLE BAKE

MAKES 2 SERVINGS

With the beef stew already made, you'll find the hands-on, in-the-kitchen time cut to a minimum for this dinner. If you have 1 cup of any leftover cooked medium-sized pasta such as ziti, bow ties, or short spiral pasta, you can use it here instead of the noodles and save the step of cooking the pasta. And if reduced-fat Monterey Jack cheese is what's in your refrigerator, use that instead of the cheddar cheese.

2   ounces pappardelle pasta or extra-wide egg noodles

2½ cups reserved Beef, Beer, and Vegetable Stew (page 90)

1   (8-ounce) can low-sodium tomato sauce

¼   cup shredded reduced-fat cheddar cheese

1   tablespoon plain dry bread crumbs

1   tablespoon grated Parmesan cheese

1. Preheat the oven to 350°F. Lightly spray a 1½-quart casserole dish with nonstick spray.

2. Bring a pot of lightly salted water to a boil. Cook the pasta according to package directions; drain.

3. Meanwhile, combine the stew and tomato sauce in a medium saucepan over medium heat. Cook, stirring occasionally, until heated through, about 10 minutes. Stir in the cooked pasta and heat through.

4. Combine the cheddar cheese, bread crumbs, and Parmesan cheese in a small bowl. Pour the beef mixture into the casserole dish; sprinkle with the cheese mixture.

5. Lightly spray a sheet of foil with nonstick spray, then place it over the casserole dish. Bake 10 minutes, then uncover and bake until the casserole is heated through and the cheese is melted, about 5 minutes longer.

Per serving (½ of casserole): 456 Cal, 10 g Fat, 3 g Sat Fat, 0g Trans Fat, 90 mg Chol, 826 mg Sod, 54 g Carb, 8 g Fib, 36g Prot, 251 mg Calc. *POINTS* value: *9.*

———————————— • ————————————

TIP Spraying the foil with nonstick spray before covering the casserole prevents the cheese from sticking to the foil.

CRUSTY PORK TENDERLOIN WITH SWEET POTATO AND APPLE

MAKES 2 SERVINGS (PLUS LEFTOVER PORK)

Pork is considered lean meat and a smart choice in a healthy eating plan. Good lean pork cuts to try are tenderloin, loin roasts, and loin chops. Avoid overcooking it by using an instant-read meat thermometer. Granny Smith used to be the old standby apple for baking, but for a fresh taste, try Braeburn, Pink Lady, or Fuji—all of which are great either eaten raw or baked. Whichever apple you choose there is no need to peel it for this recipe. Complete the meal with steamed spinach.

1   tablespoon chopped fresh parsley

1   teaspoon grated lemon zest

1   garlic clove, minced

1   teaspoon extra-virgin olive oil

$\frac{1}{2}$ teaspoon salt

$\frac{1}{2}$ teaspoon coarsely ground pepper

1   (1-pound) pork tenderloin, trimmed of all visible fat

1   large (10-ounce) sweet potato, peeled and cut crosswise into 8 slices

1   tablespoon water

1   apple, cut into 6 wedges

1   teaspoon packed dark brown sugar

$\frac{1}{8}$ teaspoon cinnamon

1. Preheat the oven to 450°F. Spray a 9 x 13-inch baking dish with nonstick spray.

2. Mix the parsley, lemon zest, garlic, oil, $\frac{1}{4}$ teaspoon of the salt, and the pepper to a paste in a small bowl. Place the pork in the baking dish. Spread the parsley mixture evenly over the top of the pork and let stand 5–10 minutes.

3. Meanwhile, place the sweet potato slices and water in a small microwavable casserole dish. Cover and microwave on High until parcooked, 3 minutes; drain.

4. Place the sweet potato slices and apple wedges around the pork. Lightly spray the sweet potato and apple with nonstick spray, then sprinkle with the sugar, cinnamon, and remaining $\frac{1}{4}$ teaspoon salt. Roast until an instant-read thermometer inserted in the center of the pork registers 160°F for medium and the sweet potato and apple are tender, about 30 minutes. Cover the pork lightly with a foil tent and let stand 5 minutes.

5. Cut the pork crosswise in two. Wrap half and refrigerate for up to 3 days for later use. Cut the remaining pork into 6–8 slices and serve with the sweet potato and apple.

Per serving (3-4 pork slices, 4 sweet potato slices, and 3 apple wedges): 325 Cal, 6 g Fat, 2 g Sat Fat, 0 g Trans Fat, 72 mg Chol, 500 mg Sod, 40 g Carb, 5 g Fib, 28 g Prot, 49 mg Calc. *POINTS* value: *6.*

**Crusty Pork Tenderloin with
Sweet Potato and Apple**

PORK FRIED RICE

MAKES 2 SERVINGS 🥄 🕐 🗑

If you get a chance, boil the white rice for this recipe the night before and refrigerate it—day-old rice is drier and makes a better fried rice. If you are boiling the rice just before making this recipe, spread the hot cooked rice on a baking sheet to cool (about 10 minutes) before using it. Substitute a chopped small onion for the scallions, if scallions aren't a staple in your pantry.

½ pound reserved cooked pork from Crusty Pork Tenderloin with Sweet Potato and Apple (page 92)

1 teaspoon Asian (dark) sesame oil

2 scallions, thinly sliced

1 celery stalk, thinly sliced

1 teaspoon grated peeled fresh ginger

1 cup frozen peas and carrots, thawed

1 cup cooked white rice

2 teaspoons reduced-sodium soy sauce

1 teaspoon bottled oyster sauce

Pinch crushed red pepper

¼ cup fat-free egg substitute

⅛ teaspoon salt

1. Scrape away and discard the topping from the pork. Cut the pork into thin strips; set aside.

2. Heat the sesame oil in a medium nonstick skillet over medium-high heat. Add the scallions, celery, and ginger. Stir-fry until softened, about 2 minutes. Add the pork strips, peas and carrots, rice, soy sauce, oyster sauce, and crushed red pepper. Stir-fry until heated through, about 3 minutes. Transfer the mixture to a warm serving bowl.

3. Spray the same skillet with nonstick spray and set over medium-high heat. Add the egg substitute and salt. Cook, stirring occasionally, until scrambled and cooked through, about 1 minute. Stir the egg into the rice mixture and serve at once.

Per serving (1¾ cups): 347 Cal, 8 g Fat, 2 g Sat Fat, 0 g Trans Fat, 72 mg Chol, 711 mg Sod, 34 g Carb, 4 g Fib, 34 g Prot, 65 mg Calc. *POINTS* value: 7.

———————————————— ● ————————————————

TIP For extra flavor, without increasing the *POINTS* value, add a tablespoon or two of chopped fresh cilantro or basil at the last minute.

Pork Fried Rice

CHICKEN CORDON BLEU WITH ARUGULA AND GRAPES

MAKES 2 SERVINGS (PLUS 2 LEFTOVER CHICKEN ROLLS)

Comté cheese is a wonderfully flavorful cheese in the Gruyère family from the Franche Comté region of France, where it has been made for centuries. It is available in many supermarkets and is worth hunting down. If you can't find it, substitute Gruyère cheese. To round out the meal, you can serve each portion with 1/2 cup cooked egg noodles and up the *POINTS* value by 2.

4   (1/4-pound) thin-sliced chicken cutlets, lightly pounded

2   (1-ounce) slices cooked ham, cut in half crosswise

1   ounce Comté cheese, shredded

3   tablespoons fat-free egg substitute

1   teaspoon Dijon mustard

1/4 cup plain dry bread crumbs

1   teaspoon canola oil

1/2 cup reduced-sodium chicken broth

2   tablespoons dry white wine

2   cups lightly packed arugula or baby spinach leaves

1/3 cup seedless red grapes

1. Place a piece of ham and one-fourth of the cheese on each of the chicken cutlets. Roll the cutlets up and secure with wooden toothpicks.

2. Lightly beat the egg substitute and mustard with a fork on a plate. Spread the bread crumbs on a sheet of wax paper. Dip the chicken rolls in the egg substitute mixture, turning to coat all sides. Then dip in the bread crumbs, lightly pressing the crumbs to adhere to the chicken.

3. Heat the oil in a large nonstick skillet over medium heat. Add chicken rolls and cook, turning occasionally with tongs, until golden on all sides, about 5 minutes. Add the broth and wine; bring to a boil. Reduce the heat and simmer, covered, until the chicken is cooked through, 8–10 minutes.

4. Remove 2 of the chicken rolls and set aside to cool. Transfer the 2 remaining chicken rolls to 2 serving plates; keep warm. Add the arugula and grapes to the skillet and cook, stirring frequently, until the arugula is wilted, about 2 minutes. Spoon the arugula and grape sauce evenly over each chicken roll on a serving plate. Serve at once. Cover and refrigerate the 2 cooled chicken rolls for up to 2 days for later use.

Per serving (1 chicken roll and 1/3 cup sauce): 266 Cal, 9 g Fat, 3 g Sat Fat, 0 g Trans Fat, 84 mg Chol, 474 mg Sod, 11 g Carb, 1 g Fib, 34 g Prot, 140 mg Calc. *POINTS* value: *6.*

CHICKEN CORDON BLEU SANDWICHES

MAKES 2 SERVINGS ✖ 🕒

If you like, you can make these into open-face sandwiches: Simply spread the mayonnaise and mustard evenly over all four halves of the bread rolls then top evenly with the spinach, roasted red pepper, and finally the pinwheel slices of chicken cordon bleu.

2	reserved chicken rolls from Chicken Cordon Bleu with Arugula and Grapes (page 96)
2	sesame kaiser rolls
2	teaspoons low-fat mayonnaise
2	teaspoons Dijon mustard
1	cup fresh baby spinach leaves
1	jarred roasted red pepper, cut in half

1. Cut the chicken rolls into ¼-inch-thick pinwheel slices and set aside.

2. Split the kaiser rolls in half horizontally. Spread the mayonnaise evenly over the bottom halves of each roll and spread the mustard evenly over the top halves of each roll.

3. Arrange the chicken evenly on the bottom halves of the bread rolls. Top each evenly with the spinach and a red pepper half. Place the bread roll tops over the filling.

Per serving (1 sandwich): 422 Cal, 12 g Fat, 3 g Sat Fat, 1 g Trans Fat, 84 mg Chol, 1043 mg Sod, 38 g Carb, 2 g Fib, 39 g Prot, 176 mg Calc. *POINTS* value: *9.*

———————————— ● ————————————

TIP You can serve these sandwiches at once. Or pack them for lunch—they keep well, wrapped in foil or plastic wrap, in the refrigerator for up to 24 hours.

Roast Chicken Breast with Potatoes and Asparagus

MAKES 2 SERVINGS (PLUS LEFTOVER CHICKEN)

A hefty dose of pungent mustard and aromatic fresh tarragon gives clout to this one-pot meal. The whole-grain mustard looks wonderful on the chicken, but regular Dijon mustard would be fine, too. One-pound mesh bags of small confetti potatoes (white, purple, and red) are available in many supermarkets today and are great for adding menu variety in households of two. If you can't find them, use small white or red potatoes.

2   tablespoons whole-grain Dijon mustard

1   tablespoon chopped fresh tarragon, or 1 teaspoon dried

1   garlic clove, minced

1   teaspoon extra-virgin olive oil

1   teaspoon honey

½   teaspoon salt

1   skinless bone-in chicken breast (about 1¼ pounds)

4   small (about ½ pound) white, purple, or red potatoes, cut into 1-inch chunks

2   carrots, cut into ½-inch-thick slices

½   pound fresh asparagus

2   lemon wedges

1. Preheat the oven to 400°F. Spray a 9 x 13-inch baking dish with nonstick spray.

2. Combine the mustard, tarragon, garlic, oil, honey, and salt in a medium bowl. Add the chicken; toss well to coat.

3. Place the chicken, breast-side up, in the center of the baking dish. Add the potatoes and carrots to the mustard mixture in bowl; toss well to coat. Arrange the potatoes and carrots around the chicken. Roast 25 minutes.

4. Meanwhile trim and discard the tough ends of the asparagus; cut into 2-inch lengths. Add to potatoes and carrots in baking pan, stirring to coat asparagus. Roast until an instant-read thermometer inserted in the chicken breast registers 170°F and the vegetables are tender, about 12 minutes longer.

5. Cut the chicken breast in two. Wrap and refrigerate half for up to 3 days for later use. Thinly slice the remaining half chicken breast from the bone (discard the bones) and serve with the vegetables and lemon wedges.

Per serving (about 5 thin slices chicken and 1½ cups vegetables): 292 Cal, 5 g Fat, 1 g Sat Fat, 0 g Trans Fat, 62 mg Chol, 568 mg Sod, 35 g Carb, 5 g Fib, 27 g Prot, 61 mg Calc. *POINTS value: 5.*

TIP An easy way to rid asparagus stalks of their tough ends is to break each one off with your fingers at the point where the stem snaps easily. If the chicken is cooked before the vegetables are tender, remove the chicken and cook the vegetables a few minutes longer.

Roast Chicken Breast with Potatoes and Asparagus

Chinese Chicken in Acorn Squash

MAKES 2 SERVINGS

Increase the fun factor of this delicious fusion of east and west by eating it with chopsticks—they are a perfect tool for grabbing chunks of chicken and vegetables, as well as scraping out the tender squash from its shell. If you don't have toasted sesame seeds on hand, you can toast them in the dry skillet before cooking the vegetables. Simply cook over low heat, shaking the skillet frequently, until the seeds are toasted, about 3 minutes. Then spread the seeds on a small plate to cool.

½ reserved cooked chicken breast from Roast Chicken Breast with Potatoes and Asparagus (page 98)

1 (1½-pound) acorn squash, halved lengthwise and seeded

¼ cup water

2 teaspoons Asian (dark) sesame oil

2 cups small broccoli florets

1 medium red onion, halved lengthwise, then sliced crosswise

½ red bell pepper, seeded and cut into ½-inch pieces

1½ tablespoons bottled black bean sauce

1 teaspoon grated peeled fresh ginger

1 teaspoon toasted sesame seeds

1. Cut the chicken from the bone (discard the bones). Cut the chicken into ¼-inch chunks and set aside.
2. Place the squash halves, cut-side down, in a microwavable dish with a lid. Add the water and cover. Microwave on High until the squash is tender when pierced with a knife, about 12 minutes. Set aside with the lid on to keep warm.
3. Meanwhile, heat the oil in a nonstick skillet over high heat until a drop of water sizzles. Add broccoli, onion, and bell pepper; stir-fry until lightly browned and crisp-tender, about 4 minutes. Reduce the heat to low and add the black bean sauce, ginger, 3 tablespoons of cooking liquid from the squash, and the chicken. Cook, stirring frequently, until heated through, about 3 minutes.
4. Place each of the squash halves, cut-side up, on a plate. Spoon the chicken mixture evenly into the squash halves. Sprinkle with the sesame seeds.

Per serving (1 squash half with generous 1½ cups filling): 407 Cal, 11 g Fat, 2 g Sat Fat, 0 g Trans Fat, 62 mg Chol, 677 mg Sod, 53 g Carb, 8 g Fib, 30 g Prot, 188 mg Calc. *POINTS* value: *8.*

TIP The size and weight of acorn squash can vary, so use the scales in the produce section of the supermarket to check the weight.

Chinese Chicken in
Acorn Squash

TUNA STEAKS WITH CREAMY MUSTARD SAUCE

MAKES 2 SERVINGS (PLUS 2 LEFTOVER TUNA STEAKS) ⏲

Pan-searing nicely chars the outside of the tuna steaks, which we cook rare to medium-rare with a little red still in the center. If you prefer your tuna well done, simply increase the cooking time. Serve each portion with ½ cup of hot cooked egg noodles (and up the *POINTS* value by 2) and a cup of steamed broccoli florets.

1   teaspoon Worcestershire sauce

1   teaspoon whole-grain Dijon mustard

¼   teaspoon salt

4   (5-ounce) yellowfin tuna steaks, ¾-inch thick

2   teaspoons olive oil

3   scallions, sliced

1   garlic clove, minced

½   cup reduced-sodium chicken broth

1   teaspoon cornstarch

3   tablespoons fat-free half-and-half

3   tablespoons brandy (optional)

1. Combine the Worcestershire sauce, mustard, and salt in the bottom of a shallow dish. Add the tuna, turning to coat both sides; let stand 5 minutes to marinate.

2. Heat 1 teaspoon of the oil in a large nonstick skillet over medium heat. Add tuna and cook until golden on the outside but still a little red in the center, 2-3 minutes on each side. Transfer 2 of the tuna steaks to a plate to cool, then cover and refrigerate for up to 2 days for later use. Transfer the 2 remaining tuna steaks to 2 serving plates; cover lightly with a foil tent and keep warm.

3. Heat the remaining 1 teaspoon oil in the same skillet. Add the scallions and garlic; cook, stirring constantly, until fragrant, about 1 minute. Add the broth and bring to a boil. Reduce the heat and simmer, uncovered, until the mixture is reduced by about one-third, about 2 minutes.

4. Dissolve the cornstarch in the half-and-half in a small bowl. Stir into the broth mixture in the skillet. Cook, stirring constantly, until the sauce simmers and thickens. Remove the foil from the 2 reserved tuna steaks; pour the sauce over the tuna.

5. Heat the brandy (if using) in a very small saucepan (do not boil); ignite and pour over the tuna.

Per serving (1 tuna steak and 3 tablespoons sauce): 218 Cal, 6 g Fat, 1 g Sat Fat, 0 g Trans Fat, 78 mg Chol, 450 mg Sod, 5 g Carb, 1 g Fib, 31 g Prot, 104 mg Calc. *POINTS* value: *5.*

TUNA PAD THAI

MAKES 2 SERVINGS ♦ ◷

Lively flavors abound in this favorite Thai dish. Asian fish sauce with its pungent, salty-sweet taste is essential to Thai and other Southeast Asian cuisines. It's available in the Asian food aisle of most supermarkets. You can substitute lean strips of cooked pork or chicken for the tuna if you like. Or, for a vegetarian version, substitute chunks of firm tofu for the tuna and ½ teaspoon of salt for the fish sauce.

2   reserved tuna steaks from Tuna Steaks with Creamy Mustard Sauce (page 102)

3   ounces rice noodles or linguine

1½ tablespoons fresh lime juice

1   tablespoon Asian fish sauce (nam pla)

2   teaspoons packed light brown sugar

1   teaspoon chile garlic sauce

1   teaspoon reduced-sodium soy sauce

1   teaspoon canola oil

2   scallions, thinly sliced

1   garlic clove, minced

1   cup fresh bean sprouts

1   carrot, shredded

1   large egg, lightly beaten

1   tablespoon unsalted dry-roasted peanuts, chopped

1   tablespoon coarsely chopped fresh cilantro

1. Break the tuna into small chunks; set aside. Cook the rice noodles according to package directions. Drain in a colander under cold running water to stop the cooking and set aside.

2. Combine the lime juice, fish sauce, sugar, chile garlic sauce, and soy sauce in a small bowl; set aside.

3. Heat the oil in a large nonstick skillet over medium heat. Add the scallions, and garlic. Cook, stirring frequently, until fragrant, about 1 minute. Add the bean sprouts and carrot; cook until softened, about 2 minutes. Add the egg, stirring gently, until it begins to set, about 30 seconds. Add the lime juice mixture and cook, stirring until the sugar dissolves, about 30 seconds. Add the tuna and rice noodles; cook, tossing gently, until mixed and heated through, about 3 minutes. Sprinkle with the peanuts and cilantro just before serving.

Per serving (1½ cups): 487 Cal, 13 g Fat, 2 g Sat Fat, 0 g Trans Fat, 184 mg Chol, 854 mg Sod, 53 g Carb, 4 g Fib, 40 g Prot, 97 mg Calc. *POINTS* value: *10*.

Coconut Shrimp with Tangy Apricot Dipping Sauce

MAKES 2 SERVINGS (PLUS LEFTOVER SHRIMP)

This all-time favorite is usually deep-fried, but baking in a hot oven with a touch of nonstick spray does the trick here. To help the coating stick to the shrimp, be sure to pat the shrimp dry with paper towels before tossing with the egg. These make great hors d'oeuvres too—served piping hot or even after sitting at room temperature for an hour or so.

½ cup flaked unsweetened coconut

⅓ cup all-purpose flour

¾ teaspoon salt

⅛ teaspoon crushed red pepper

1 large egg

1 pound jumbo shrimp, peeled (tails left on), deveined, butterflied, and patted dry

¼ cup apricot all-fruit spread

1 tablespoon prepared horseradish

1 teaspoon teriyaki or soy sauce

1. Preheat the oven to 450°F. Spray a baking sheet with nonstick spray.

2. Combine the coconut, flour, salt, and crushed red pepper on a plate.

3. Beat the egg in a medium bowl. Add the shrimp and toss to coat. Lift each shrimp from the egg, letting the excess egg drip off the shrimp, then coat in the coconut mixture, pressing to adhere. Place shrimp on the baking sheet in a single layer. Lightly spray with nonstick spray. Bake until the shrimp are golden on the outside and opaque in the center, about 10 minutes.

4. Meanwhile to make apricot dipping sauce, combine the apricot spread, horseradish, and teriyaki sauce in a small bowl.

5. Transfer half of the cooked shrimp to a plate to cool. Then cover with plastic wrap and refrigerate for up to 2 days for later use. Serve the remaining shrimp with the apricot sauce.

Per serving (5–6 shrimp and 2 ½ tablespoons sauce): 283 Cal, 9 g Fat, 6 g Sat Fat, 0 g Trans Fat, 160 mg Chol, 726 mg Sod, 36 g Carb, 4 g Fib, 16 g Prot, 53 mg Calc. *POINTS* value: *6.*

TIP Butterflying shrimp exposes more surface area of the shrimp to hold the delicious coating. To butterfly, place the shrimp on a cutting board and with the tip of a sharp knife, slice along the back outer edge of the shrimp half way through the shrimp.

SHRIMP, BLACK BEAN, AND MANGO SALAD

MAKES 2 SERVINGS ✖

Delicious leftover coconut shrimp, canned black beans, frozen corn, and bagged salad greens make this dinner-in-a-dash a cinch to put together. Serve with 2 breadsticks—the cracked-pepper variety are good here—they'll up the *POINTS* value by 1.

½ pound reserved cooked shrimp from Coconut Shrimp with Tangy Apricot Dipping Sauce (page 104)

¼ cup finely chopped red onion

1 tablespoon chopped fresh cilantro

2 teaspoons fresh lime juice

1 teaspoon extra-virgin olive oil

⅛ teaspoon salt

⅛ teaspoon ground cumin

1 cup canned black beans, rinsed and drained

½ cup fresh or thawed frozen corn

½ cup fresh mango chunks

3 cups bagged leafy salad greens

1. Remove the coconut shrimp from the refrigerator to come to room temperature for about 20 minutes.

2. Meanwhile, combine the onion, cilantro, lime juice, oil, salt, and cumin in a medium bowl. Gently stir in the black beans, corn, and mango.

3. Divide the greens between 2 salad plates. Spoon half of the black-bean mixture (about 1 cup) on each plate of greens. Place the coconut shrimp (5 to 6) on top of each and serve at once.

Per serving (1 salad): 403 Cal, 12 g Fat, 7 g Sat Fat, 0 g Trans Fat, 160 mg Chol, 1087 mg Sod, 52 g Carb, 11 g Fib, 25 g Prot, 144 mg Calc. *POINTS* value: *8*.

———————————————•———————————————

TIP A mango is ripe and ready to use when it yields to gentle pressure but is not too soft. To ripen a hard mango, let it sit on a counter or in a fruit bowl at room temperature for a day or two. To speed up the ripening process, place it in a paper bag.

LINGUINE AND MEATBALLS WITH ZUCCHINI

MAKES 2 SERVINGS (PLUS LEFTOVER MEATBALLS)

We feel that once you have your hands in a meatball mixture, it's just as easy to make extra for another meal. Our second meal takes on a South-of–the-border flavor and becomes a comforting soup (page 108).

1   teaspoon olive oil

1   large onion, chopped

3   garlic cloves, minced

¾   pound ground skinless turkey breast

3   tablespoons seasoned dry bread crumbs

1   large egg, lightly beaten

¼   teaspoon freshly ground pepper

1   (14½-ounce) can Italian stewed tomatoes

2   tablespoons dry red wine

1   zucchini, diced

1   tablespoon chopped fresh basil, or 1 teaspoon dried

⅓   (9-ounce) package fresh refrigerated linguine

1. Preheat the oven to 400°F. Spray a shallow baking pan with nonstick spray.

2. Heat the oil in a nonstick Dutch oven over medium heat. Add onion and garlic. Cook, stirring frequently, until golden, about 6 minutes. Transfer half of the onion mixture to a large bowl. Set aside the remaining onion mixture in the Dutch oven.

3. To the onion mixture in the bowl, add the turkey, bread crumbs, egg, and pepper; mix well. Shape into 20 meatballs. Place the meatballs on the baking pan and bake until lightly browned and cooked through, about 20 minutes. Transfer 10 of the meatballs to a plate to cool, then cover and refrigerate for up to 2 days, or wrap and freeze for up to 2 months, for later use.

4. Meanwhile, add the tomatoes, wine, and zucchini to the onion mixture in the Dutch oven; bring to a boil. Reduce the heat and simmer, uncovered, until the mixture thickens slightly and the zucchini softens, about 20 minutes. Add the remaining 10 meatballs to the sauce and heat through. Stir in the basil.

5. Cook the linguine according to package directions; drain. Serve the meatballs and the sauce over the linguine.

Per serving (5 meatballs, 1 cup sauce, and ¾ cup linguine): 420 Cal, 5 g Fat, 1 g Sat Fat, 0 g Trans Fat, 109 mg Chol, 829 mg Sod, 62 g Carb, 6 g Fib, 31 g Prot, 125 mg Calc. *POINTS* value: *8.*

Linguine and Meatballs with Zucchini

Mexican Meatball Soup

MAKES 2 SERVINGS

You can make this comforting soup with leftover meatballs and a few pantry shelf ingredients in just about 30 minutes. If you add the meatballs to the soup while they are still frozen, simmer them for an extra 5 to 10 minutes.

1   (14½-ounce) can Mexican stewed tomatoes

1   (14-ounce) can reduced-sodium chicken broth

3   tablespoons long-grain white rice

½   (10-ounce) package frozen chopped spinach, thawed and squeezed dry

⅓   cup fresh or frozen corn kernels

1   small jalapeño pepper, seeded and finely chopped (wear gloves to prevent irritation)

10 reserved meatballs from Linguine and Meatballs with Zucchini (page 106)

2   tablespoons shredded reduced-fat Monterey-Jack or cheddar cheese

1   scallion, thinly sliced

1. Bring the tomatoes, broth, and rice to a boil in a medium saucepan. Reduce heat and simmer, covered, until the rice is tender, about 20 minutes.

2. Add the spinach, corn, and jalapeño pepper; return to a boil. Add the meatballs, reduce the heat, and simmer until heated through, about 5 minutes.

3. Ladle the soup evenly into 2 bowls. Sprinkle with the cheese and scallion and serve at once.

Per serving (generous 1½ cups soup with 1 tablespoon cheese): 365 Cal, 6 g Fat, 2 g Sat Fat, 0 g Trans Fat, 114 mg Chol, 1172 mg Sod, 45 g Carb, 5 g Fib, 33 g Prot, 226 mg Calc. *POINTS* value: *7.*

TIP The jalapeño pepper adds a nice punch to this soup. If you prefer a mild-tasting soup, omit it. If you prefer a moderately fiery soup, substitute pepper-Jack cheese for the Monterey Jack cheese and omit the jalapeño pepper.

Mexican Meatball Soup

MOROCCAN THREE-BEAN STEW

MAKES 2 SERVINGS (PLUS LEFTOVER STEW)

Frozen extra-fine French green beans are long, thin and bright green and are a good choice for this dish. You can dish up each portion of this stew with ⅓ cup of cooked whole-wheat couscous and a tablespoon of toasted pine nuts. Be sure to up the *POINTS* value by 2.

2 teaspoons olive oil

1 large onion, chopped

2 garlic cloves, minced

½ (1-pound) bag frozen sliced bell peppers

1 (14-ounce) can diced tomatoes

1 (15-ounce) can red kidney beans, rinsed and drained

1 (8-ounce) can chickpeas rinsed and drained

¼ teaspoon salt

1 cup (from a 1-pound bag) frozen French green beans

2 tablespoons raisins

¼ teaspoon ground coriander

¼ teaspoon cinnamon

⅛ teaspoon cayenne

1. Heat oil in a large nonstick saucepan over medium heat. Add the onion and garlic and cook, stirring frequently, until golden, about 8 minutes. Add the bell peppers and tomatoes; bring to a boil. Reduce the heat and simmer, uncovered, until slightly thickened, about 10 minutes. Stir in the kidney beans, chickpeas, and salt. Cook until heated through, stirring occasionally, about 5 minutes.

2. Transfer half of the bean mixture (about 2¼ cups) to a bowl; let cool. Cover and refrigerate for up to 5 days for later use.

3. Add the green beans, raisins, coriander, cinnamon, and cayenne to the remaining bean mixture in the saucepan; bring to a boil. Reduce the heat and simmer, covered, stirring occasionally, until the green beans are tender and the flavors are melded, about 10 minutes.

Per serving (1½ cups): 274 Cal, 4 g Fat, 0 g Sat Fat, 0 g Trans Fat, 0 mg Chol, 527 mg Sod, 51 g Carb, 13 g Fib, 13 g Prot, 123 mg Calc. *POINTS* value: *5.*

SPICY BEAN NACHOS

MAKES 2 SERVINGS ♦ 🍲 ⏱ 🌶

Since this easy favorite is eaten mostly with your fingers and shared from one plate, get a little closer, grab a nacho, and have fun! And be sure to arm yourselves with an extra napkin or two.

2¼ cups reserved Moroccan Three-Bean Stew (page 110)

1 tablespoon taco seasoning mix

18 baked tortilla chips (about 1½ ounces)

¼ cup reduced-fat shredded Monterey Jack cheese

1 tablespoon chopped green chiles

1 plum tomato, diced

1 scallion, thinly sliced

1. Preheat the broiler. Heat the bean stew and taco seasoning in a medium saucepan, stirring occasionally until heated through.

2. Arrange the tortilla chips in an 9-inch pie dish. Spoon the bean mixture evenly over the chips. Sprinkle with the cheese and chiles. Broil 4 inches from the heat until the filling is hot and the cheese is melted, about 2 minutes. Top with the tomato and scallion and serve at once.

Per serving (½ of nachos): 344 Cal, 7 g Fat, 2 g Sat Fat, 0 g Trans Fat, 10 mg Chol, 979 mg Sod, 55 g Carb, 12 g Fib, 17 g Prot, 209 mg Calc. *POINTS* value: *7.*

———————————— ● ————————————

TIP This is a simple way to use leftover chili of any kind—bean, beef, or chicken.

Chili-Topped Baked Potatoes

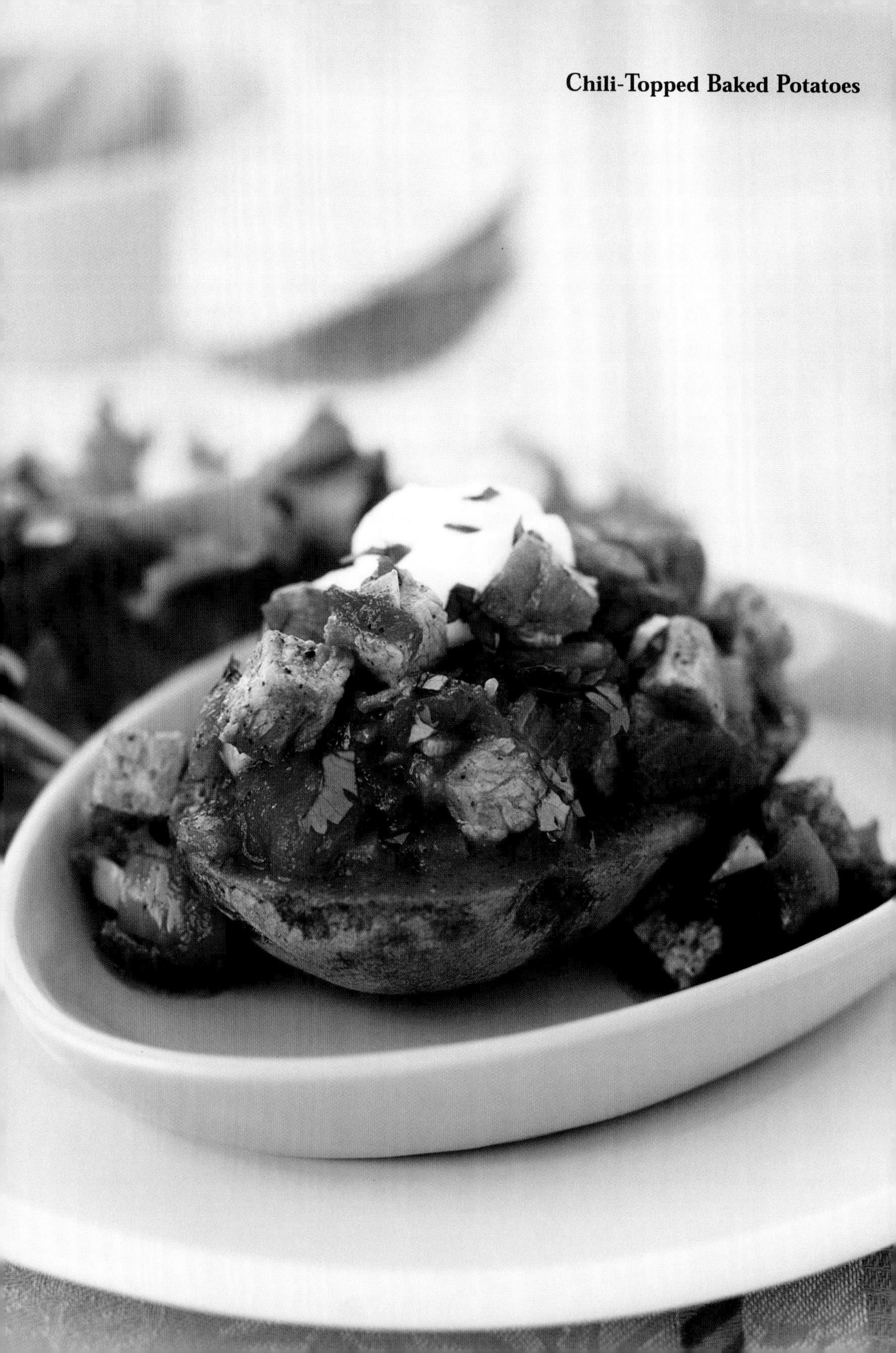

CHILI-TOPPED BAKED POTATOES

MAKES 2 SERVINGS (PLUS LEFTOVER POTATOES) 🌶 🍲 🥫

Potatoes have had a bad rap for being "fattening" for some time. However, it is usually the topping, such as butter or sour cream, that adds the calories. When served with a low-fat topping such as this chili, they make a substantial, yet trim, meal. This is a good way to use leftover chicken or turkey, while making extra potatoes for another meal at the same time.

3   (10-ounce) baking potatoes, scrubbed

1   teaspoon canola oil

1   small onion, chopped

2   garlic cloves, minced

1   (14½-ounce) can diced tomatoes with green chiles

1   medium zucchini, diced

1   teaspoon chili powder

¾   teaspoon ground cumin

¾   cup chopped cooked chicken or turkey

2   tablespoons fat-free sour cream

2   tablespoons chopped fresh cilantro

1. Preheat the oven to 425°F. Place the potatoes directly on the middle oven rack and bake until fork tender, 45–50 minutes.

2. Meanwhile, heat the oil in a nonstick saucepan over medium heat. Add the onion and garlic and cook, stirring occasionally, until golden, 7–10 minutes. Add the tomatoes, zucchini, chili powder, and cumin; bring to a boil. Reduce the heat and simmer, covered, until the zucchini is tender about 15 minutes. Add the chicken and heat through.

3. Set 2 of the potatoes aside until cool then wrap and refrigerate for up to 3 days for later use. Cut remaining potato lengthwise in half. Place each half on a serving plate. Spoon the chili mixture evenly over each potato half. Top each with sour cream and cilantro.

Per serving (½ potato, 1½ cups chili, and 1 tablespoon sour cream): 338 Cal, 7 g Fat, 1 g Sat Fat, 0 g Trans Fat, 46 mg Chol, 650 mg Sod, 50 g Carb, 6 g Fib, 22 g Prot, 136 mg Calc. *POINTS* value: *7.*

BAKED POTATO SOUP

MAKES 2 SERVINGS 🍲 🕐

The baking potato, such as Idaho and russet, is low in moisture and high in starch, allowing it to fall apart easily and making it ideal for baking or mashing in soups such as this.

2   reserved baked potatoes from Chili-Topped Baked Potatoes (page 113)

2   strips bacon

4   scallions, thinly sliced

3   garlic cloves, minced

1   (14-ounce) can reduced-sodium chicken broth

½   teaspoon salt

⅛   teaspoon cayenne

½   cup fat-free half-and-half

¼   cup chopped fresh parsley

1. Coarsely chop the potatoes (leave the skin on); set aside.

2. Cook the bacon in a medium nonstick saucepan until crisp; drain the bacon on paper towels and set aside. Pour off and discard all but 1 teaspoon of the bacon drippings from the saucepan.

3. Add 2 of the scallions and the garlic to the drippings in saucepan. Cook, stirring occasionally, until softened, about 3 minutes. Add the broth, salt, cayenne, and chopped potatoes, mashing the potatoes slightly with a wooden spoon to break them up a bit. Bring the mixture to a boil. Reduce the heat and simmer, uncovered, until heated through, 2–3 minutes. Stir in the half-and-half and parsley; return to a simmer. Serve the soup sprinkled with the bacon and the remaining 2 sliced scallions.

Per serving (2¼ cups): 397 Cal, 7 g Fat, 2 g Sat Fat, 0 g Trans Fat, 7 mg Chol, 1176 mg Sod, 66 g Carb, 7 g Fib, 14 g Prot, 153 mg Calc. *POINTS* value: *7.*

Baked Potato Soup

EVERYDAY ENTRÉES

MEAT, POULTRY, FISH, AND VEGETARIAN MEALS

Flank Steak with Roasted
Asparagus and Red Peppers

FLANK STEAK WITH ROASTED ASPARAGUS AND RED PEPPERS

MAKES 2 SERVINGS

This steak is at its best if allowed to marinate overnight. If, however, you don't get to it the night before, don't worry because it takes only minutes to prepare the three-ingredient marinade and the steak in the morning. And, if that doesn't fit your schedule, 20 to 30 minutes of marinating also will do the trick. We use jumbo asparagus because they cook in the same amount of time as bell peppers. If only thin asparagus is available in your market, add them to the roasting pan after the bell peppers have roasted for 5 minutes.

1   tablespoon reduced-sodium soy sauce

2   large garlic cloves, minced

1   teaspoon ground cumin

1/2 pound flank steak, about 1/2-inch thick, trimmed of all visible fat

1   bunch fresh jumbo asparagus (1 pound), trimmed

2   small red bell peppers, seeded and quartered lengthwise

1 1/2 teaspoons olive oil

1/4 teaspoon salt

2   tablespoons snipped fresh chives

1. Combine the soy sauce, garlic, and cumin in a zip-close plastic bag; add the steak. Squeeze out the air and seal the bag; turn and rub to coat the steak. Refrigerate, turning the bag occasionally, at least 20 minutes or overnight.

2. Preheat the oven to 425°F. Toss the asparagus and bell peppers with the oil and salt in a shallow roasting pan. Spread the vegetables out in an even layer. Roast until tender and slightly caramelized, 15–17 minutes.

3. Meanwhile, remove the steak from the bag and pat dry with paper towels. Spray a nonstick or cast-iron skillet with nonstick spray and set over medium-high heat. Add the steak and cook until done to taste, about 4 minutes on each side for medium-rare. Transfer the steak to a carving board, cover loosely with a foil tent, and let stand 5 minutes. Cut the steak, on the diagonal, into 10 slices.

4. Add the chives to the vegetables and toss to mix. Serve the vegetables with the steak.

Per serving (5 slices steak and 1 1/4 cups vegetables): 264 Cal, 12 g Fat, 4 g Sat Fat, 0 g Trans Fat, 64 mg Chol, 492 mg Sod, 11 g Carb, 3 g Fib, 29 g Prot, 50 mg Calc. *POINTS* value: *6.*

EASY THAI BEEF SALAD

MAKES 2 SERVINGS ♦ ☕ ⏱

Fish sauce—made from anchovies, water, and salt—is found in Asian markets and in the ethnic section of most supermarkets. *Nam pla* is the name for Thai fish sauce and *nuoc mam* is Vietnamese fish sauce; they are interchangeable. Thai bird chile peppers are small, pointed, extremely hot peppers that are red, orange, or green. If unavailable, you can substitute the more readily available serrano chile pepper, which has a bit less heat.

1   (6-ounce) filet mignon, about 1-inch thick

¼   teaspoon salt

2   tablespoons fresh lime juice

1   tablespoon Asian fish sauce

1   tablespoon sugar

1   tablespoon finely chopped peeled fresh ginger

1   large garlic clove, minced

1   Thai bird chile pepper, seeded and minced (wear gloves to prevent irritation)

5   cups shredded romaine lettuce

1   5-inch-long piece seedless cucumber, halved lengthwise and sliced crosswise

⅓   cup sliced radishes

⅓   cup fresh cilantro leaves

⅓   cup fresh mint leaves

1. Heat a medium nonstick or cast-iron skillet over medium-high heat. Sprinkle the steak with the salt. Add the steak to the skillet and cook until done to taste, about 3 minutes on each side for rare. Cover the steak with a foil tent and let stand 5 minutes. Cut the steak, across the grain, into ¼-inch-thick slices; let cool slightly.

2. Meanwhile, combine the lime juice, fish sauce, sugar, ginger, garlic, and chile pepper in a large serving bowl. Add the beef, lettuce, cucumber, radishes, cilantro, and mint; toss to mix. Serve at once.

Per serving (3½ cups): 206 Cal, 7 g Fat, 2 g Sat Fat, 0 g Trans Fat, 48 mg Chol, 627 mg Sod, 16 g Carb, 4 g Fib, 22 g Prot, 86 mg Calc. *POINTS* value: *4.*

Easy Thai Beef Salad

REUBEN QUESADILLA

MAKES 2 SERVINGS 🍲 ⏱

The Reuben, a classic sandwich in delicatessens and diners across America, is outrageously high in fat and calories—and fabulously delicious. As the story goes, it was created for a leading lady in a Charlie Chaplin film in 1914. We have drastically slimmed down the sandwich by turning it into a quesadilla and using reduced-fat corned beef, which you can find at the deli counter in supermarkets and in specialty-food stores.

¼ pound sliced reduced-fat corned beef, chopped

¼ cup packaged reduced-sodium sauerkraut, drained and squeezed dry

½ apple, cored and chopped

4 (6-inch) low-fat flour tortillas

1 tablespoon honey mustard

¼ cup shredded pepperjack cheese

1. Combine the corned beef, sauerkraut, and apple in a small bowl.

2. Lightly spray one side of the tortillas with nonstick spray. Heat a large nonstick skillet over medium heat. Cook the tortillas (without turning them), sprayed-side down, in batches, just until light golden on the bottom, 1–2 minutes.

3. Spread the mustard on the toasted side of each tortilla and sprinkle evenly with the cheese. Cover half of each tortilla with one-fourth of the corned beef mixture (about ⅓ cup); fold the unfilled half of each tortilla over the filling. Lightly spray same pan with nonstick spray and set over medium heat. Return the tortillas to the skillet and cook until golden on the bottom, about 1½ minutes. With a spatula, carefully turn the quesadillas and cook until toasted on the other side, about 1½ minutes longer.

Per serving (2 quesadillas): 328 Cal, 12 g Fat, 5 g Sat Fat, 1 g Trans Fat, 42 mg Chol, 1251 mg Sod, 34 g Carb, 4 g Fib, 19 g Prot, 187 mg Calc. *POINTS* value: 7.

PICADILLO AND RICE

MAKES 2 SERVINGS ♦ ▮

Picadillo is a favorite dish in many Spanish-speaking countries. Variations abound but there are a few ingredients they all contain: ground meat, tomatoes, garlic, and onions. The remaining ingredients usually reflect the region in which the dish is prepared. Nonpareil capers are very small capers. You can substitute regular capers and chop them.

½ cup long-grain white rice

½ pound lean ground beef (10% or less fat)

1 medium onion, finely chopped

½ teaspoon ground cumin

⅛ teaspoon cinnamon

1 cup canned diced tomatoes with green chiles

¼ cup water

1 rounded tablespoon dark raisins

1 teaspoon nonpareil capers, drained

¼ teaspoon salt

1. Cook the rice according to package directions, omitting the salt, for 3–4 minutes less than directed. Remove from the heat and let stand, covered, about 5 minutes.

2. Meanwhile, spray a large nonstick skillet with nonstick spray and set over medium-high heat. Add the beef and onion; cook, breaking the meat up with a wooden spoon, until browned, about 8 minutes. Drain off any fat.

3. Stir in the cumin and cinnamon; cook 30 seconds. Add the tomatoes, water, raisins, capers, and salt; bring to a boil. Reduce the heat to medium and cook until slightly reduced, 4–5 minutes. Serve the picadillo over the cooked rice.

Per serving (1 cup picadillo and ⅔ cup rice): 443 Cal, 9 g Fat, 3 g Sat Fat, 0 g Trans Fat, 65 mg Chol, 742 mg Sod, 60 g Carb, 3 g Fib, 30 g Prot, 75 mg Calc. *POINTS* value: *9.*

———————————•———————————

TIP Picadillo makes a great company dish, as it is easy to prepare and serve a large batch—so double or triple this recipe if you like. You can make it a day ahead; the flavor will only improve.

PORK AND EGGPLANT BOLOGNESE

MAKES 2 SERVINGS

Bolognese, a richly flavored meat sauce that is a staple throughout northern Italy, has as many variations as there are cooks who prepare this time-honored dish. Usually made with ground meat, tomato, carrot, celery, onion, garlic, wine, and milk for creamy sweetness, bolognese sauce is cooked very slowly to give the ingredients all the time they need to develop and mellow.

¼ pound lean ground pork

1 medium onion, finely chopped

1 large garlic clove, minced

1 (1-pound) eggplant, peeled and cut into ½-inch dice

¼ cup water

2 tablespoons dry white wine

1 (8-ounce) can tomato sauce

¼ teaspoon fennel seeds, crushed

¼ teaspoon salt

⅛ teaspoon freshly ground pepper

2 cups mini rigatoni (4 ounces)

¼ cup fresh basil leaves, thinly sliced

1. Spray a large nonstick skillet with nonstick spray and set over medium-high heat. Add the pork and onion and cook until well browned, about 5 minutes. Add the garlic and cook, stirring constantly, until fragrant, about 30 seconds. Stir in the eggplant and water. Cover the skillet, reduce the heat to medium-low, and cook until the eggplant is tender, 12–15 minutes.

2. Add the wine to the skillet and boil 30 seconds. Stir in the tomato sauce, fennel, salt, and pepper; bring to a boil. Reduce the heat and simmer, covered, until slightly thickened, 15–18 minutes.

3. Meanwhile, cook the pasta according to package directions, omitting the salt.

4. Stir the basil into the sauce. Drain the pasta, return to the pot, and immediately stir in 1 cup of the sauce. Spoon the pasta mixture into 2 shallow bowls and top with the remaining sauce.

Per serving (scant 2 cups pasta and sauce): 427 Cal, 6 g Fat, 2 g Sat Fat, 0 g Trans Fat, 37 mg Chol, 1013 mg Sod, 70 g Carb, 9 g Fib, 24 g Prot, 66 mg Calc. *POINTS* value: *8.*

PORK WITH SOFT TACOS

MAKES 2 SERVINGS

Monterey Jack is a California cheese that was developed in the 19th century by David Jacks. It is an unaged, soft, yellow cheese with a mild flavor. Pepperjack cheese is Monterey Jack cheese with tasty bits of jalapeño peppers. It melts beautifully and makes a great addition to sandwiches such as this one.

1   teaspoon olive oil

1   (8-ounce) package sliced white mushrooms

1   small onion, finely chopped

½   pound pork tenderloin, chopped

¼   teaspoon salt

¼   teaspoon cumin seeds

½   cup roasted-tomato or regular salsa

3   (6-inch) low-fat flour tortillas

¼   cup shredded pepperjack cheese

1. Heat the oil in a large nonstick skillet over high heat. Add the mushrooms and onion and cook until tender, about 6 minutes; transfer to a bowl.

2. Sprinkle the pork with the salt and add to the skillet; sprinkle with the cumin. Cook over high heat, stirring, until the pork is browned, about 3 minutes. Stir in the salsa and the mushroom mixture and cook until heated through, about 2 minutes. Transfer to a bowl and wipe the skillet clean with paper towels.

3. Spray the skillet with nonstick spray and set over medium heat. Cook tortillas, one at a time, just until golden on the bottom, about 1½ minutes. Place the tortillas, toasted-side up, on a work surface. Spread the pork mixture (about ⅔ cup) over half of each tortilla and sprinkle with one-third of the cheese. Fold the unfilled tortilla half over the filling.

4. Spray the skillet with nonstick spray and set over medium heat. Add the tacos to the skillet and cook, turning once with a large spatula, until golden, about 1 minute on each side.

Per serving (1½ tacos): 399 Cal, 14 g Fat, 5 g Sat Fat, 1 g Trans Fat, 84 mg Chol, 880 mg Sod, 32 g Carb, 4 g Fib, 37 g Prot, 190 mg Calc. *POINTS* value: *8.*

Pork with Soft Tacos

PORK TENDERLOIN WITH TROPICAL COUSCOUS

MAKES 2 SERVINGS ○

Pork tenderloin is a very lean, very tender, and very tasty cut of meat. One tenderloin usually weighs between 12 and 16 ounces. For this recipe, choose a 1-pound tenderloin and cut it in half crosswise. Use the thick half ("head") here and the tapered portion ("tail") when you need chopped or diced pork (see Pork with Soft Tacos, page 125).

1   (½-pound) piece pork tenderloin

1   large garlic clove, minced

1½ teaspoons minced peeled fresh ginger

½ + ⅛ teaspoon salt

¾   cup + 2 tablespoons orange-mango or orange-tangerine juice

½   cup couscous

1   scallion, sliced

1½ teaspoons olive oil

1. Cut the pork crosswise into 8 slices. Mash the garlic, ½ teaspoon of the ginger, and ½ teaspoon of the salt in a small dish until a paste forms. Rub the mixture into both sides of the pork slices; set aside for 5 minutes.

2. Meanwhile, to make the couscous, bring ¾ cup of the juice, the remaining 1 teaspoon ginger, and the remaining ⅛ teaspoon salt to a boil in a small saucepan. Stir in the couscous and cover; remove from the heat and let stand 5 minutes. Fluff with a fork, then stir in the remaining 2 tablespoons juice and the scallion. Transfer to a serving bowl; keep warm.

3. Meanwhile, heat the oil in a large nonstick skillet over medium-high heat. Place the pork in the skillet in one layer. Cook until browned on the outside and the pork has lost its pink color throughout, about 2 minutes on each side. Transfer the pork to a platter and serve with the couscous.

Per serving (4 slices pork and ¾ cup couscous): 397 Cal, 8 g Fat, 2 g Sat Fat, 0 g Trans Fat, 72 mg Chol, 796 mg Sod, 47 g Carb, 3 g Fib, 32 g Prot, 32 mg Calc. *POINTS* value: *8.*

GREEN CHICKEN AND EDAMAME SALAD

MAKES 2 SERVINGS 🍲 🕐

Edamame (the Japanese name for fresh green soybeans) deserve a lot of respect: The Chinese and Japanese have revered soybeans, in a wide variety of forms, for centuries. They use mature soybeans to make many soy products, including tofu, soy milk, miso, soybean oil, and soy sauce. *Edamame* are picked before they are fully mature and left in their fuzzy bright green pods. They are high in protein and fiber, and are very digestible. They are found in the freezer section of most supermarkets and health-food stores and can be purchased fresh most of the year in Asian markets.

2   tablespoons orange juice

1   tablespoon fresh lime juice

1   tablespoon chopped
    fresh cilantro

½   teaspoon grated peeled
    fresh ginger

½   teaspoon salt

1   cup diced cooked
    chicken breast

¾   cup shelled edamame
    (fresh green soy beans),
    cooked

½   small avocado, pitted, peeled,
    and diced

Whisk together the orange juice, lime juice, cilantro, ginger, and salt in a serving bowl until blended. Add the chicken and soybeans; toss to coat. Add the avocado; toss gently to mix.

Per serving (1 cup): 291 Cal, 14 g Fat, 2 g Sat Fat, 0 g Trans Fat, 57 mg Chol, 658 mg Sod, 13 g Carb, 5 g Fib, 30 g Prot, 116 mg Calc. *POINTS* value: *6*.

———————————— • ————————————

TIP Cook frozen *edamame* according to the package directions. If you purchase them fresh, steam them for about 15 minutes, then pop them out of their pods (discard the pods). You might like to cook extra to serve as a tasty snack.

GARLIC-AND-THYME CHICKEN WITH POTATOES

MAKES 2 SERVINGS

Nothing satisfies quite as much as a one-pot meal. It makes less work for the cook, and all of the tempting flavors of the dish blend together for rich flavor. Topping the chicken with slices of lemon does two things. It imparts a lovely citrus flavor to the chicken and it helps to keep the chicken moist. Red potatoes work well here, but you can also use Yukon Gold potatoes, if you like.

2 garlic cloves

1 tablespoon fresh thyme leaves, or 1 teaspoon dried

$\frac{1}{2}$ + $\frac{1}{8}$ teaspoon salt

2 (9-ounce) bone-in chicken breast halves

$\frac{1}{8}$ teaspoon freshly ground pepper

$\frac{1}{2}$ lemon, cut into 4 slices

2 (5-ounce) red potatoes, each cut into eighths

1 small onion, chopped

1 teaspoon olive oil

1. Preheat the oven to 350°F.

2. Using a large chef's knife, chop the garlic, thyme, and $\frac{1}{2}$ teaspoon of the salt until a thick paste forms. With your fingers, gently separate the chicken skin from the breast meat; spread the garlic paste over the breast meat. Smooth the skin back into place and season with the pepper. Place the lemon slices on top of the breasts, slightly overlapping them, and place the breasts at one end of a broiler pan.

3. Toss together the potatoes, onion, oil, and remaining $\frac{1}{8}$ teaspoon salt on the opposite side of the broiler pan; spread the mixture to form one layer.

4. Bake until the chicken is cooked through and the potatoes are just tender, about 30 minutes. Preheat the broiler. Broil the chicken and potato mixture 6 inches from the heat until the chicken and potatoes are browned, 3–4 minutes. Remove the skin before eating.

Per serving (1 chicken breast half and 1 cup vegetables): 376 Cal, 8 g Fat, 2 g Sat Fat, 0 g Trans Fat, 103 mg Chol, 841 mg Sod, 34 g Carb, 4 g Fib, 41 g Prot, 52 mg Calc. *POINTS* value: *7.*

Garlic-and-Thyme
Chicken with Potatoes

HAM STEAK WITH APPLE-CIDER SAUCE AND MASHED BUTTERNUT SQUASH

MAKES 2 SERVINGS

This recipe is ideal in the autumn when apple cider is freshly made in farmers' markets and the array of apples and winter squash seems endless. Look for butternut squash that has a long neck because the smaller the bulb the fewer the seeds. Here we use apple juice and apple cider—you can use fresh apple cider, which is made by pressing the juice out of apples, or hard cider, which is fresh apple cider that has been allowed to ferment, making it mildly alcoholic.

1 teaspoon unsalted butter

1 (1¼-pound) butternut squash, peeled, seeded, and diced

¼ cup apple juice

1 large apple, such as Fuji or Braeburn, peeled, cored, and diced

1 small onion, chopped

¾ cup fresh or hard cider

1 tablespoon cider vinegar

1 tablespoon packed brown sugar

1 (1-pound) hickory-smoked, reduced-sodium, thin-cut, bone-in ham steak, cut in half, bone discarded

1. Melt the butter in large nonstick skillet over medium heat. Add the squash and cook, covered, stirring occasionally, until tender, about 12 minutes. Add the apple juice; cover and simmer until a small amount of liquid remains, 2–3 minutes. Transfer the squash to a bowl and mash until smooth; keep warm.

2. Wipe the skillet clean with paper towels. Spray with nonstick spray and set over medium heat. Add the apple and onion; cook, covered, stirring occasionally, until softened and slightly browned, about 4 minutes. Add the cider, vinegar, and sugar; bring to a boil. Reduce the heat and simmer, uncovered, until the sauce is slightly reduced, 3–4 minutes.

3. Meanwhile, spray another large skillet with nonstick spray and set over medium heat. Add the ham and cook until browned and heated through, 1–2 minutes on each side. Transfer the ham to a platter; spoon the sauce over the ham. Serve with the butternut squash.

Per serving (1 piece ham, ⅔ cup squash, ½ cup sauce): 409 Cal, 6 g Fat, 2 g Sat Fat, 0 g Trans Fat, 60 mg Chol, 961 mg Sod, 58 g Carb, 6 g Fib, 22 g Prot, 129 mg Calc. *POINTS* value: *8.*

SESAME CHICKEN

MAKES 2 SERVINGS ♦ ☕

Here, chicken is browned in a skillet, then transferred to the oven where it finishes cooking. This classic restaurant technique keeps chicken moist and tender. Most skillets are ovenproof up to 350°F, but if you're not sure about your skillet, wrap the handle with a double thickness of foil. Cajun seasoning can be found in the spice section of supermarkets. It is a flavorful mix of garlic, bell peppers, chile peppers, black pepper, cayenne, oregano, salt, and paprika.

2   (5-ounce) skinless boneless
    chicken breast halves

½   cup low-fat buttermilk

2   tablespoons plain dry
    bread crumbs

1   tablespoon sesame seeds

½   teaspoon Cajun seasoning

2   teaspoons olive oil
    or canola oil

1. Combine the chicken and buttermilk in a small bowl; cover and refrigerate, about 20 minutes.

2. Preheat the oven to 350°F.

3. Mix together the bread crumbs, sesame seeds, and Cajun seasoning on a sheet of wax paper. Lift a chicken breast from the buttermilk, allowing the excess buttermilk to drip off. Coat the chicken on both sides with the crumb mixture, pressing gently so it adheres. Repeat with the remaining chicken; discard any remaining buttermilk and crumb mixture.

4. Heat the oil in a medium nonstick skillet over medium-high heat. Add the chicken and cook until golden, 2–3 minutes on each side. Transfer the skillet to the oven and bake until the chicken is cooked through, about 10 minutes.

Per serving (1 chicken breast half): 281 Cal, 12 g Fat, 2 g Sat Fat, 0 g Trans Fat, 87 mg Chol, 302 mg Sod, 7 g Carb, 1 g Fib, 34 g Prot, 73 mg Calc. *POINTS* value: *6.*

———————————— ● ————————————

TIP It's easy to cook an extra chicken breast here to make a tasty sandwich another day. Simply cut the chicken crosswise into thin slices, top with lightly dressed salad greens, and place between toasted slices of Italian peasant bread.

Spicy Molasses–
Barbecued Drumsticks

Spicy Molasses–Barbecued Drumsticks

MAKES 2 SERVINGS ♦ ▯

You can make this delicious barbecue sauce in a large batch and refrigerate it in a covered container for up to two weeks. It's great on either grilled or broiled chicken, beef, or pork. Two types of molasses are available in supermarkets: unsulphured light (mild) and blackstrap. For most cooking and baking, light molasses is used. You might like to serve these drumsticks with chopped romaine lettuce and shredded carrot tossed with a low-fat blue cheese dressing.

3   tablespoons bottled
    chili sauce

1½ tablespoons plain or seasoned
    cider vinegar

1   tablespoon light molasses

1   teaspoon chili powder

½   teaspoon minced chipotle
    en adobo

1   garlic clove, minced

4   (3-ounce) chicken drumsticks,
    skin removed

1. To make the molasses barbecue sauce, combine the chili sauce, vinegar, molasses, chili powder, chipotle en adobo, and garlic in a small saucepan; bring to a boil. Reduce the heat to low and simmer, stirring, until thickened, 2–3 minutes.

2. Meanwhile, spray the grill rack with nonstick spray and prepare the grill. Place the chicken on the grill and cook, turning occasionally, about 8 minutes. Brush the chicken with the barbecue sauce. Cook, turning the chicken, until deeply glazed and cooked through, 5–6 minutes longer.

Per serving (2 drumsticks): 204 Cal, 4 g Fat, 1 g Sat Fat, 0 g Trans Fat, 98 mg Chol, 402 mg Sod, 16 g Carb, 1 g Fib, 26 g Prot, 56 mg Calc. *POINTS* value: *4*.

———————————— ● ————————————

TIP If you prefer, you can broil the chicken 6 inches from the heat until cooked through, about 6 minutes on each side. Then brush the chicken with the sauce and broil, turning occasionally, about 4 minutes longer.

CHICKEN BREASTS WITH CAPER SAUCE

MAKES 2 SERVINGS

These chicken breasts are coated with a rich (in flavor only) sauce that can be partly made ahead and finished last minute in the pan. Capers are the flower bud of a bush, native to the Mediterranean. Nonpareil capers, the smallest variety, are grown in the south of France. The capers from Italy are large and are often packed in salt, so always rinse before using.

1   cup reduced-sodium chicken broth

½   teaspoon sherry vinegar

4   large garlic cloves

5   whole black peppercorns

1   bay leaf

2   (5-ounce) skinless boneless chicken breast halves

¼   teaspoon salt

⅛   teaspoon freshly ground pepper

1   teaspoon olive oil

1   teaspoon capers, drained

1   teaspoon butter, softened

1   teaspoon all-purpose flour

1. Bring the broth, vinegar, garlic, peppercorns, and bay leaf, to a boil in a small saucepan. Reduce the heat and simmer until the liquid is reduced to about ¾ cup and the garlic is very tender, 8–9 minutes. Discard the peppercorns and bay leaf; puree the garlic mixture in a blender.

2. Sprinkle the chicken with the salt and pepper. Heat the oil in a medium nonstick skillet over medium heat. Add chicken and cook until browned, about 5 minutes on each side. Add the garlic mixture and capers; partially cover and cook, turning the chicken, until heated through, 2–3 minutes longer.

3. Meanwhile, mix the butter and flour in a small custard cup to form a paste. Stir it into the sauce until blended and smooth. Simmer until the sauce is thickened, about 1 minute.

Per serving (1 chicken breast half and ⅓ cup sauce): 210 Cal, 9 g Fat, 3 g Sat Fat, 0 g Trans Fat, 74 mg Chol, 649 mg Sod, 4 g Carb, 0 g Fib, 28 g Prot, 29 mg Calc. *POINTS* value: *5*.

ASIAN CHICKEN AND GREENS

MAKES 2 SERVINGS

The marinade in this recipe is bold enough to flavor chicken in just 15 minutes. A portion of the marinade performs double-duty—we add it to the delicious orange-and-peanut–flavored salad dressing. If you prefer to assemble the chicken the night before, you can marinate it in a zip-close plastic bag in the refrigerator overnight.

2 tablespoons seasoned rice vinegar

1 tablespoon reduced-sodium soy sauce

2 large garlic cloves, minced

1½ teaspoons grated peeled fresh ginger

½ teaspoon sugar

2 (5-ounce) skinless boneless chicken thighs

1 tablespoon orange juice

1 teaspoon smooth peanut butter

1 (5-ounce) bag spring mix salad greens

½ small onion, cut into thin wedges

1 small carrot, sliced

1. To make the marinade, combine the vinegar, soy sauce, garlic, ginger, and sugar in a medium bowl. Transfer 1 tablespoon of the marinade to a microwavable cup. Add the chicken to the marinade in the bowl; toss to coat. Refrigerate 15 minutes.

2. Add the orange juice and peanut butter to the marinade in the cup; heat in the microwave on High just until the marinade is warm and the peanut butter is melted, about 15 seconds; whisk until smooth.

3. Line the broiler pan with foil; preheat the broiler. Pat the chicken dry with paper towels; place in the broiler pan. Broil 5 inches from the heat until browned, about 7 minutes. Turn the chicken and broil until cooked through, about 1 minute longer. Let stand 5 minutes. Slice the chicken and toss with the salad greens, onion, carrot, and dressing in a large bowl until combined.

Per serving (2 cups): 168 Cal, 7 g Fat, 2 g Sat Fat, 0 g Trans Fat, 43 mg Chol, 211 mg Sod, 9 g Carb, 3 g Fib, 17 g Prot, 66 mg Calc. *POINTS* value: *3.*

———————————— • ————————————

TIP When buying fresh ginger look for smooth, shiny skin without wrinkles. Fresh ginger can be stored up to several weeks wrapped in paper towels in an unsealed plastic bag in the refrigerator. Or place sliced or minced peeled ginger in a plastic freezer bag and freeze for up to several months.

SOUTH-OF-THE-BORDER PASTA AND CHICKEN

MAKES 2 SERVINGS 🔥 🍲

If you like, use leftover chicken breast or the breast from a rotisserie chicken for this dish; just be sure to remove the skin. You can also use cut-up cooked chicken that is available in the meat department of most supermarkets. This recipe can easily be doubled, which makes it a great dish for company.

1⅓ cups radiatore or medium shells (4 ounces)

2 tablespoons fresh lime juice

1½ teaspoons extra-virgin olive oil

½ teaspoon sugar

½ teaspoon salt

1 cup diced cooked chicken breast

½ medium red bell pepper, seeded and cut into small dice

½ medium green or yellow bell pepper, seeded and cut into small dice

½ small red onion, thinly sliced

½ medium jalapeño pepper, seeded and minced (wear gloves to prevent irritation)

2 tablespoons finely chopped fresh cilantro

1. Cook the pasta according to package directions, omitting the salt, if desired. Drain and rinse under cold running water; drain again.

2. Meanwhile, toss together the lime juice, oil, sugar, and salt in a medium bowl. Add the chicken, bell peppers, onion, jalapeño pepper, cilantro, and pasta; toss to coat.

Per serving (2 cups): 398 Cal, 8 g Fat, 2 g Sat Fat, 0 g Trans Fat, 57 mg Chol, 649 mg Sod, 52 g Carb, 4 g Fib, 29 g Prot, 33 mg Calc. *POINTS* value: *8.*

———————•———————

TIP To keep fresh cilantro, trim the stem ends and put it into a glass that contains about one inch of cold water. Cover the cilantro with a plastic bag and place in the refrigerator. Before using cilantro, be sure to rinse well as it tends to be sandy.

WARM TURKEY AND NECTARINE SALAD WITH ORANGE VINAIGRETTE

MAKES 2 SERVINGS 🍲 🕐

When choosing nectarines, take a good whiff. They should have a wonderful perfumed fragrance, even if the nectarines are very firm. If they smell good, they will be flavorful and ripen nicely on a kitchen counter. If they don't have a fragrance, they were picked too soon and will never be sweet. Peaches make a fine substitute for nectarines, so use them if they seem a better choice in your market.

2 tablespoons orange juice

1½ tablespoons white balsamic vinegar

1 tablespoon minced shallots

2 teaspoons extra-virgin olive oil

½ teaspoon honey

½ teaspoon salt

2 (4-ounce) turkey breast cutlets

⅛ teaspoon freshly ground pepper

1 large bunch watercress, tough stems discarded, leaves rinsed

2 small nectarines, cut in ½-inch-thick wedges

½ cup matchstick-size pieces peeled jicama or unpeeled seedless cucumber

1. To make the orange vinaigrette, whisk together the orange juice, vinegar, shallots, 1 teaspoon of the oil, the honey, and ¼ teaspoon of the salt in a large bowl until blended; set aside.

2. Heat the remaining 1 teaspoon oil in a large nonstick skillet set over medium-high heat. Sprinkle the turkey cutlets with the remaining ¼ teaspoon salt and the pepper. Add to the skillet and cook until just cooked through, about 2 minutes on each side. Transfer the cutlets to a plate and let cool 5 minutes. Slice crosswise into strips.

3. Re-whisk the vinaigrette; add the watercress, nectarines, jicama, and turkey to the dressing; toss to mix well.

Per serving (3 cups): 232 Cal, 6 g Fat, 1 g Sat Fat, 0 g Trans Fat, 75 mg Chol, 968 mg Sod, 16 g Carb, 4 g Fib, 29 g Prot, 121 mg Calc. *POINTS* value: *4.*

SPICY TURKEY BURGERS WITH TZATZIKI

MAKES 2 SERVINGS ♦

Tzatziki is a Greek yogurt sauce that gained popularity in the seventies when served with the gyro sandwich—a pita pocket filled with slices of flavorful grilled lamb, topped with tomato, grilled onion, and a dollop of *tzatziki*. It is a perfect low-fat, yet creamy, foil to these zesty burgers. You might like to serve the burgers with toasted pita bread (1 pita per serving will up the *POINTS* value by 2) and cherry tomatoes.

½ pound lean ground
    turkey breast

1   small zucchini, coarsely
    shredded

1   tablespoon finely grated
    onion

1   tablespoon finely chopped
    fresh cilantro

½ small jalapeño pepper,
    seeded and minced (wear
    gloves to prevent irritation)

1   teaspoon olive oil or
    vegetable oil

½ cup plain low-fat yogurt

⅓ cup finely diced or sliced
    seeded peeled cucumber

1   small garlic clove, minced

½ teaspoon grated lime zest

1½ teaspoons fresh lime juice

1. To make the burgers, combine the turkey, zucchini, onion, cilantro, and jalapeño pepper in a bowl until well mixed. Shape into 4 patties.

2. Heat ½ teaspoon of the oil in a large nonstick skillet over medium-high heat. Add the burgers and cook until golden and cooked through, about 12 minutes, turning the burgers halfway through and adding the remaining ½ teaspoon oil to the pan after turning them.

3. Meanwhile, to make the tzaziki sauce, stir together the yogurt, cucumber, garlic, lime zest, and juice in a small bowl. Serve with the burgers.

Per serving (2 burgers and generous ⅓ cup sauce): 199 Cal, 4 g Fat, 1 g Sat Fat, 0 g Trans Fat, 79 mg Chol, 96 mg Sod, 8 g Carb, 1 g Fib, 31 g Prot, 142 mg Calc. *POINTS* value: *4.*

Spicy Turkey Burgers
with Tzatziki

Halibut with Scallion-Mashed Potatoes

Halibut with Scallion-Mashed Potatoes

MAKES 2 SERVINGS

We like using Yukon Gold potatoes for mashing. This all-purpose potato has a medium amount of starch and makes delectably creamy mashed potatoes. Its flesh can range in color from an appetizing butter-yellow to golden, and its taste is superior to that of other mashing potatoes. Be sure to buy authentic Yukon Gold potatoes—look for them by name. Steamed whole, small carrots make a pretty and tasty go-along here.

10 ounces Yukon Gold potatoes, peeled and cut into 1½-inch chunks

⅓ cup fat-free milk

⅓ cup sliced scallions

1 teaspoon extra-virgin olive oil

½ teaspoon salt

Coarsely ground black pepper

2 (5-ounce) center-cut halibut fillets, about ¾-inch thick, skin removed

2 teaspoons finely chopped fresh parsley

1. Bring the potatoes with enough water to cover to a boil in a medium saucepan. Cook until tender, about 15 minutes; drain. Combine the milk, scallions, oil, and ¼ teaspoon of the salt in the same pot (no need to clean it) and cook until the milk is hot. Add the potatoes to the milk mixture and mash until fluffy. Season to taste with the pepper.

2. Meanwhile, preheat the oven to 300°F. Line a baking sheet with heavy-duty foil; spray with nonstick spray. Place the fish on the baking sheet. With your fingertips, spread the parsley on top of the fillets; sprinkle with the remaining ¼ teaspoon salt and season with pepper.

3. Bake the fish until just opaque in the center, about 18 minutes. Serve with the mashed potatoes.

Per serving (1 fish fillet and scant ⅔ cup potatoes): 256 Cal, 4 g Fat, 1 g Sat Fat, 0 g Trans Fat, 62 mg Chol, 715 mg Sod, 29 g Carb, 3 g Fib, 26 g Prot, 92 mg Calc. *POINTS* value: *5.*

———————————— ● ————————————

TIP Cooking fish at a lower-than-usual temperature results in a more evenly cooked, moist fillet that is hard to accidentally overcook.

FLOUNDER WITH MANGO SALSA

MAKES 2 SERVINGS

Look for thick fish fillets for the most succulent flakes of fish—a delectable contrast to the crisp cornmeal crust.

1   large mango, peeled, pitted, and cut into small dice

2   teaspoons + 3 tablespoons fresh lime juice (about 2 limes)

1   teaspoon finely chopped shallot

1   teaspoon minced jalapeño pepper (wear gloves to prevent irritation)

1   teaspoon sugar

1   tablespoon reduced-sodium soy sauce

1   tablespoon minced onion

2   (½-pound) flounder, red snapper, or catfish fillets, skin removed

2   tablespoons cornmeal

½   teaspoon salt

1½   teaspoons olive oil or vegetable oil

1. To make the mango salsa, combine the mango, 2 teaspoons of the lime juice, the shallot, jalapeño pepper, and sugar in a bowl; set aside.

2. Stir together the remaining 3 tablespoons lime juice, the soy sauce, and onion on a large platter. Add the fish and turn several times to coat; refrigerate 15 minutes.

3. Meanwhile, combine the cornmeal and salt on a plate. Pat the fish dry with paper towels; coat on both sides with the cornmeal, shaking off the excess.

4. Heat ¾ teaspoon of the oil in a large nonstick skillet over medium-high heat. Add the fish and cook until golden on the bottom, about 4 minutes. With a large spatula, carefully turn the fish; add the remaining ¾ teaspoon oil to the pan, tilting the pan so the oil can go underneath the fish. Cook until the fish is just opaque in the center, about 3 minutes longer. Serve the fish with the mango salsa.

Per serving (1 fish fillet and ½ cup salsa): 301 Cal, 6 g Fat, 1 g Sat Fat, 0 g Trans Fat, 99 mg Chol, 957 mg Sod, 25 g Carb, 3 g Fib, 37 g Prot, 44 mg Calc. *POINTS* value: *6.*

———————————— ● ————————————

TIP   There are two ways to get the most juice out of limes: Roll the limes back and forth on a work surface, gently pressing down on the fruit, or put the limes into a microwave oven and cook on High for 20 seconds, until slightly warm. Cut the limes in half and squeeze out the juice.

BROILED FLOUNDER WITH SAUTÉED ESCAROLE AND SHELL PASTA

MAKES 2 SERVINGS

Why purchase bread crumbs when you can make superior crumbs at home with very little effort? Save up leftover bread heels and slices. Let the bread dry out thoroughly, then break it into chunks and process in the food processor. Transfer the crumbs to a covered container and store in the freezer. If you prefer your bread crumbs white, cut the crusts from the bread before you let it dry out.

½ cup baby shells or ditalini

1 bunch (1-pound), escarole, trimmed, cut crosswise in half, and rinsed (do not shake dry)

1 carrot, finely diced

1 large garlic clove, minced

⅓ cup reduced-sodium chicken broth

1 flat anchovy, drained and minced

2 (½-pound) flounder fillets

⅛ teaspoon salt

Freshly ground pepper

2 tablespoons plain dry bread crumbs

½ teaspoon olive oil

1. Cook the pasta according to package directions, omitting the salt, if desired. Drain and set aside.
2. Place the escarole in a large Dutch oven. Cook, covered, over medium-high heat until wilted about 4 minutes; drain. Wipe the pot dry. Spray the pot with nonstick spray and set over medium heat. Add the carrot and garlic; cook until carrot is bright orange and garlic is golden, about 2 minutes. Add the escarole, broth, and anchovy to the Dutch oven; simmer, covered, until the flavors blend, 4–5 minutes. Stir in the pasta.
3. Meanwhile, line a broiler pan with heavy-duty foil and spray with nonstick spray; preheat the boiler. Place the fish fillets in the broiler pan in one layer. Sprinkle the fish with the salt and season with pepper. Mix the bread crumbs and the oil in a cup until the crumbs are evenly moistened; sprinkle over the fillets. Lightly spray the crumb topping with nonstick spray. Broil the fish 5 inches from the heat until just opaque in the center and the crumbs are deep golden, about 4 minutes. Serve with the escarole and pasta mixture.

Per serving (1 fish fillet and 1½ cups escarole-pasta mixture): 455 Cal, 6 g Fat, 2 g Sat Fat, 0 g Trans Fat, 113 mg Chol, 586 mg Sod, 52 g Carb, 10 g Fib, 51 g Prot, 189 mg Calc. *POINTS* value: *9.*

SEARED TUNA WITH CARROT PUREE

MAKES 2 SERVINGS

Everyday carrots take on a taste of the exotic when ginger and cumin are added. Be sure the carrots are very tender before processing them or you won't get a really smooth puree. The carrot puree can be made up to three days ahead and kept in the refrigerator in an airtight container.

1   teaspoon butter

1   teaspoon grated peeled
    fresh ginger

½   teaspoon cumin seeds

2   large carrots, cut lengthwise
    in half and sliced crosswise

¾   cup reduced-sodium
    chicken broth

⅔   cup water

1   teaspoon sugar

Pinch + ½ teaspoon salt

2   (4-ounce) tuna steaks,
    ¾-inch thick

¼   teaspoon coarsely ground
    black pepper

1. To make the carrot puree, melt the butter in a medium saucepan over medium heat. Add the ginger and cumin; sauté until just fragrant, about 1 minute. Add the carrots; reduce the heat to medium-low and cook, covered, until the carrots turn deep orange, about 8 minutes.

2. Add the broth and water to the carrots. Reduce the heat to low and cook, covered, until the carrots are almost tender, about 20 minutes. Uncover and cook until there is ¼ inch of liquid remaining in the pan, 5–7 minutes longer. Transfer the carrots and liquid to a food processor or blender; add the sugar and a pinch salt. Pulse until smooth, scraping down the side of the bowl if necessary.

3. Sprinkle the tuna on both sides with ½ teaspoon of the salt and the pepper. Spray a large nonstick skillet with nonstick spray and set over medium-high heat. Add the tuna and cook until browned on the outside and slightly rosy in the center, about 2 minutes on each side. Serve with the carrot puree.

Per serving (1 tuna steak and ⅔ cup carrot puree): 218 Cal, 8 g Fat, 3 g Sat Fat, 0 g Trans Fat, 72 mg Chol, 1018 mg Sod, 10 g Carb, 2 g Fib, 24 g Prot, 44 mg Calc. *POINTS* value: *5.*

TIP   We recommend not overcooking tuna. For medium tuna, cook it until still slightly rosy in the middle, about 2 minutes on each side. If you prefer your tuna rare, cook it until still bright red in the center, 1–2 minutes on each side. Let the tuna rest for a few minutes before serving.

Shrimp with Black Beans

The heat of jalapeño peppers varies. Sometimes they are very hot and sometimes they are surprisingly mild. Take a little taste of the pepper after you mince it. If it has a nice bite, use half, as directed in the recipe. If it seems to lack punch, use the whole pepper. If possible, purchase a red jalapeño pepper, which is a green jalapeño that has been allowed to ripen. It will add nice color to the dish.

1 teaspoon olive oil

1 medium onion, chopped

½ small jalapeño pepper, minced (wear gloves to prevent irritation)

½ pound peeled and deveined jumbo shrimp

1 (15-ounce) can black beans, rinsed and drained

3 tablespoons reduced-sodium chicken broth or water

2 tablespoons sweet orange marmalade

Juice of 1 lime

1 tablespoon finely chopped fresh cilantro

1. Heat the oil in a large nonstick skillet over medium-high heat. Add the onion and jalapeño pepper and cook until the onion is translucent, 3–5 minutes. Add the shrimp and cook until golden and just opaque in the center, about 3 minutes, turning once halfway through.
2. Add the beans, broth, marmalade, lime juice, and cilantro to the skillet, bring to a boil. Reduce heat and simmer, until just heated through, about 1 minute.

Per serving (1½ cups): 392 Cal, 4 g Fat, 1 g Sat Fat, 0 g Trans Fat, 161 mg Chol, 849 mg Sod, 58 g Carb, 11 g Fib, 31 g Prot, 152 mg Calc. *POINTS* value: *7.*

Shrimp and White Beans over Spinach Fettuccine

MAKES 2 SERVINGS 🔥 ⏲

The size of jumbo shrimp varies from fish market to fish market. Usually, there are between 16 and 20 to the pound. Fish and shellfish need to be stored in the coldest part of the refrigerator: The storage temperature should be between 35° and 40°F. If your refrigerator is warmer than that, you may want to store fish (still in its wrapping) on ice, replenishing the ice as it melts.

2	ounces spinach fettuccine
1	tablespoon olive oil
1	medium onion, finely chopped
1	cup finely chopped fennel
2	large garlic cloves, minced
1/4	cup dry white wine
2/3	cup canned small white beans, rinsed and drained
1/2	pound peeled and deveined jumbo shrimp
2/3	cup reduced-sodium chicken broth
1/4	cup loosely packed fresh basil leaves, thinly sliced
1/4–1/2	teaspoon crushed red pepper

1. Cook the pasta according to package directions, omitting the salt if desired; drain. Keep warm.

2. Meanwhile, heat the oil in a large nonstick skillet over medium-high heat. Add the onion and fennel. Cook, covered, stirring occasionally until translucent, 3–5 minutes. Add the garlic and cook just until fragrant, about 30 seconds. Add the wine and bring to a boil; cook just until a small amount of the wine remains in the skillet. Stir in the beans, shrimp, broth, basil, and crushed red pepper; cover and bring to a boil. Reduce the heat and simmer, covered, until the shrimp are just opaque in the center, 3–4 minutes.

3. Transfer the pasta to a large serving bowl, top with the shrimp mixture, and toss to mix. Serve at once.

Per serving (1½ cups): 382 Cal, 10 g Fat, 2 g Sat Fat, 0 g Trans Fat, 186 mg Chol, 383 mg Sod, 43 g Carb, 7 g Fib, 30 g Prot, 146 mg Calc. *POINTS* value: *8.*

---•---

TIP You can substitute a 6-ounce can of solid white tuna packed in water for the shrimp if you like.

**Shrimp and White Beans
over Spinach Fettuccine**

Japanese Shrimp and Miso Soup

MAKES 2 SERVINGS

Miso, fermented soybean paste, is a mainstay of Japanese cuisine. White miso has a delicate flavor and is usually used to flavor soups and sauces. Yellow miso is the variety most often used in cooking, while red miso has the richest flavor. After opening miso, store sealed in the refrigerator. Ethnic grocery stores and wine shops carry Shaoxing wine: an inexpensive wine frequently used in Asian cooking.

1	teaspoon vegetable oil
1	(3½-ounce) package fresh shiitake mushrooms, stems discarded and caps sliced
1	garlic clove, minced
1	teaspoon grated peeled fresh ginger
1½	teaspoons red miso
1	(14-ounce) can reduced-sodium chicken broth
½	ounce vermicelli or capellini
½	pound peeled and deveined jumbo shrimp
1	small tomato, diced
3	tablespoons sake or Chinese Shaoxing cooking wine
1	tablespoon thinly sliced scallion

1. Heat the oil in a medium saucepan over medium heat. Add mushrooms and cook, stirring occasionally, until wilted, about 3 minutes. Stir in the garlic and ginger and cook, stirring, until fragrant, about 30 seconds. Add the miso, mashing it in; gradually add the broth and bring to a simmer.

2. Stir in the vermicelli, separating the strands with a fork, then stir in the shrimp, tomato, and sake. Return to a simmer and cook until the pasta is just tender and the shrimp are just opaque in the center, 2–3 minutes. Stir in the scallion just before serving.

Per serving (1¾ cups): 203 Cal, 5 g Fat, 1 g Sat Fat, 0 g Trans Fat, 161 mg Chol, 889 mg Sod, 13 g Carb, 2 g Fib, 25 g Prot, 57 mg Calc. *POINTS* value: *4.*

———————————————— ● ————————————————

TIP Here's an easy way to measure out just the right amount of pasta for this dish: Tightly gather enough pasta in your hand to measure ½-inch across. That should equal the half-ounce you need.

CHICKPEA BURGERS

MAKES 2 SERVINGS

These vegetarian burgers are as satisfying as any meat-based burger we know. The rich texture and taste is thanks to canned chickpeas, red curry paste, and just a bit of tahini. Red curry paste is sold in Asian food markets in large plastic containers and in some supermarkets in small jars. Curry paste usually contains galangal (a rhizome related to ginger that has a sharp lemony-pine taste), fresh or dried chiles, shrimp paste, and other flavorings.

1   (15½-ounce) can chickpeas (garbanzo beans), rinsed and drained

1   tablespoon tahini (sesame paste)

1   teaspoon red curry paste

1   teaspoon red-wine vinegar

¼   teaspoon salt

1   garlic clove, minced

1   egg white, lightly beaten

2   tablespoons plain dry bread crumbs

1   teaspoon olive oil or vegetable oil

½   cup roasted-tomato, tomatillo, or regular salsa

2   (6-inch) low-fat flour tortillas, toasted

1. Combine the chickpeas, tahini, curry paste, vinegar, and salt in a food processor and coarsely puree. Add the garlic and egg white and pulse just until combined. Shape the mixture into 4 burgers, about ½-inch thick. Put the bread crumbs on a piece of wax paper and coat the burgers on both sides.

2. Heat the oil in a large nonstick skillet over medium-high heat. Cook burgers until golden, about 3 minutes on each side. Serve with the salsa and tortillas.

Per serving (2 burgers, ¼ cup salsa, and 1 tortilla): 442 Cal, 13 g Fat, 2 g Sat Fat, 0 g Trans Fat, 0 mg Chol, 862 mg Sod, 64 g Carb, 14 g Fib, 20 g Prot, 166 mg Calc. *POINTS* value: *9.*

TIP To toast tortillas, heat a small dry nonstick skillet over medium heat. Lightly spray both sides of each tortilla with nonstick spray. Cook one at a time, in the skillet until golden, 1 to 1½ minutes on each side.

**Cavatappi with
Cauliflower Sauce**

CAVATAPPI WITH CAULIFLOWER SAUCE

MAKES 2 SERVINGS ♦ ⟶ 🗑

Old-world Italian comes to mind when considering this satisfying peasant dish, where cauliflower is cooked until it is soft enough to mash and served over curly, spiral-shaped pasta. The mash can be made up to a day ahead and refrigerated in an airtight container. Heat in a microwave dish on High, partially covered, 2 to 3 minutes, until hot, stirring halfway through the cooking.

1	teaspoon extra-virgin olive oil
2	large garlic cloves, finely chopped
1/8–1/4	teaspoon crushed red pepper
1	(10-ounce) package frozen cauliflower, thawed
1	tablespoon tomato paste
2/3	cup reduced-sodium chicken or vegetable broth
2	cups trumpetti or medium shells
2	tablespoons chopped fresh parsley

1. Heat the oil, garlic, and crushed red pepper in a large nonstick skillet over medium heat. Cook until the oil sizzles and the garlic just begins to turn golden, about 1 minute. Place the cauliflower and tomato paste on opposite sides of the skillet and cook, stirring separately, until tomato paste turns orange-gold, about 1 minute. Add the broth, stirring to blend; bring to a boil. Reduce the heat and simmer, covered, until the cauliflower is very tender, 20–23 minutes.

2. Meanwhile, cook the trumpetti according to package directions, omitting the salt; drain. Add the pasta to the cauliflower sauce and toss until mixed. Serve, sprinkled with the parsley.

Per serving (1 1/2 cups): 289 Cal, 4 g Fat, 1 g Sat Fat, 0 g Trans Fat, 0 mg Chol, 252 mg Sod, 52 g Carb, 6 g Fib, 12 g Prot, 45 mg Calc. *POINTS* value: *5.*

———————— ● ————————

TIP Cauliflower is an often-overlooked vegetable that is versatile and available year-round. When choosing it, look for a snowy white head that is free from soft spots and black marks. The leaves should look fresh and bright green.

Orzo and Broccoli Risotto

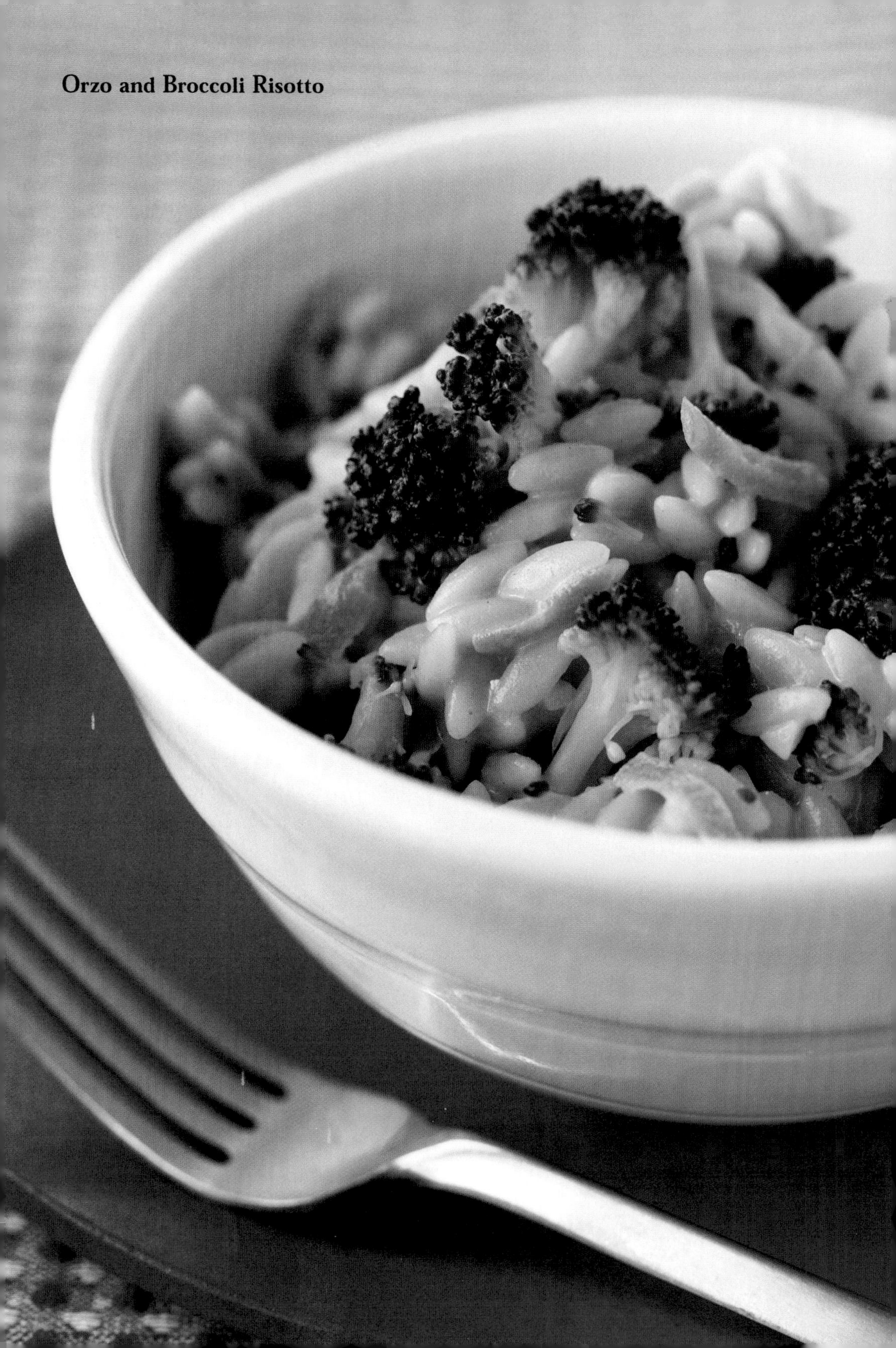

Orzo and Broccoli Risotto

MAKES 2 SERVINGS

Creamy in texture and rich in flavor, this risotto uses orzo (rice-shaped pasta) instead of Arborio (short-grain rice). Our version takes only half the time of a classic risotto but has all the delicious flavor you'd expect.

1   (14-ounce) can reduced-sodium vegetable broth

1   cup water

1   teaspoon olive oil

¼   cup coarsely shredded carrot

2   large garlic cloves, minced

1   cup orzo

½   (10-ounce) package frozen chopped broccoli, thawed and patted dry

3   tablespoons fat-free half-and-half

3   tablespoons freshly grated Parmesan cheese

1. Bring the broth and water to a boil in a small saucepan. Reduce the heat and keep at a simmer.

2. Heat the oil in a medium saucepan over medium heat. Add the carrot and garlic; cook, stirring frequently, until the carrot is bright orange and garlic is fragrant, about 1 minute. Add the orzo and cook, stirring, until it is lightly toasted, about 2 minutes.

3. Reduce the heat to medium-low. Add ½ cup of the broth mixture and stir until it is absorbed. Continue to add the broth mixture, ½ cup at a time, stirring until it is absorbed before adding more. Cook until the pasta is just slightly firm, adding the broccoli when you add the last addition of broth.

4. Stir in the half-and-half; heat 1 minute. Stir in the cheese. Spoon into shallow bowls and serve at once.

Per serving (1½ cups): 387 Cal, 8 g Fat, 3 g Sat Fat, 0 g Trans Fat, 7 mg Chol, 604 mg Sod, 60 g Carb, 5 g Fib, 19 g Prot, 220 mg Calc. *POINTS* value: *8.*

RED LENTIL AND SPINACH STEW

MAKES 2 SERVINGS ♦ 🍲 🌶 🥫

Dinner is just 25 minutes away when prepared with ingredients such as this from the pantry or freezer. Red lentils are actually delicate orange in color—not red. They create a lovely creamy base for this hearty, Indian-accented stew. Serve each portion with half of a toasted pocketless pita and up the *POINTS* value by 1.

1	teaspoon vegetable oil
1	small onion, chopped
3	medium garlic cloves, minced
1	tablespoon minced peeled fresh ginger
1	teaspoon curry powder
½	teaspoon cumin seeds
¼ to ½	teaspoon crushed red pepper
½	cup red lentils, picked over and rinsed
1	(14-ounce) can vegetable broth
1¼	cups water
1	cup frozen leaf spinach, thawed
¼	teaspoon salt

1. Heat the oil in a medium saucepan over medium heat. Add the onion and cook, stirring frequently, until translucent, 3–5 minutes. Add the garlic, ginger, curry, cumin, and crushed red pepper; cook, stirring, until fragrant, about 1 minute.

2. Add the lentils, broth, and water; bring to a simmer. Cook until the lentils are tender, about 20 minutes. Stir in spinach and salt and cook just until heated through, about 3 minutes.

Per serving (scant 2 cups): 230 Cal, 3 g Fat, 20 g Sat Fat, 0 g Trans Fat, 0 mg Chol, 1188 mg Sod, 39 g Carb, 13 g Fib, 15 g Prot, 131 mg Calc. *POINTS* value: *4.*

Red Lentil and Spinach Stew

PORTOBELLO MUSHROOMS AND BARLEY OVER MESCLUN

MAKES 2 SERVINGS

This warm salad takes advantage of the restaurant technique of reducing balsamic vinegar to a thick syrup to intensify its flavor. It's great for coating these mushrooms and creating a rich dressing.

½ cup balsamic vinegar

1½ teaspoons packed brown sugar

1 tablespoon extra-virgin olive oil

1 tablespoon finely chopped shallot

½ teaspoon salt

⅛ teaspoon freshly ground pepper

2 (6-ounce) portobello mushrooms, stems discarded, caps wiped clean

½ cup quick-cooking barley

¼ cup chopped carrot

4 cups mesclun (mixed baby salad greens) (6 ounces)

1. Preheat the oven to 425°F. Line the broiler pan with heavy-duty foil.

2. To make the dressing, bring the vinegar and sugar to a boil in a small saucepan; boil until it is reduced to 3 tablespoons, 4–5 minutes. Remove from the heat and whisk in the oil, shallot, salt, and pepper.

3. Scrape away the black "gills" from the underside of the mushroom caps with the tip of a small spoon; discard. Place the mushrooms, rounded-side up, in the broiler pan. Brush the tops of the mushrooms with 1 tablespoon of the dressing. Bake 15 minutes. Cover the mushrooms with a foil tent and set aside.

4. Meanwhile, cook the barley according to package directions, adding the carrot during the last 3 minutes of cooking time; drain.

5. Slice the mushrooms and toss with the barley and 2 tablespoons of the dressing in a bowl. Toss the mesclun with the remaining 1–2 tablespoons dressing and divide between 2 plates. Spoon the mushroom mixture on top of the salad and serve.

Per serving (2⅓ cups barley mixture and 1½ cups salad): 322 Cal, 8 g Fat, 1 g Sat Fat, 0 g Trans Fat, 0 mg Chol, 631 mg Sod, 57 g Carb, 12 g Fib, 12 g Prot, 80 mg Calc. *POINTS* value: *6*.

———————————— ● ————————————

TIP Try drizzling reduced balsamic vinegar decoratively on dinner plates around chicken or pork chops, spooning a bit of it over fresh fruit, or whisking it into a favorite salad dressing.

BLACK BEAN STEW

MAKES 2 SERVINGS ♦ ⊘ ▯

Beans, pasta, corn, and roasted garlic team up here for an easy pantry meal. Most supermarkets carry roasted garlic in jars, but it is easy to make at home if you prefer. Cut off the top fourth from as many garlic heads as you want to roast. Wrap the garlic loosely in foil and bake in a preheated 375°F oven until the garlic is very soft when poked with a wooden pick about 40 minutes. The garlic will keep for about a week, well wrapped, in the refrigerator.

1	slice bacon, chopped
²/₃	cup canned diced tomatoes with green chiles
½	cup baby shells
1	cup canned black beans, rinsed and drained
1	cup reduced-sodium chicken broth
½	cup water
1	large roasted garlic clove, mashed
½	cup frozen corn, thawed

1. Cook the bacon in a medium saucepan until crisp; drain on paper towels. Drain off and discard all but 1 teaspoon of the bacon fat from the pan. Add the tomatoes to the saucepan and simmer until slightly thickened, about 2 minutes.

2. Meanwhile, cook the pasta according to package directions, omitting the salt; drain.

3. Add the black beans, broth, water, and garlic to the tomatoes and bring to a boil. Reduce the heat and simmer 5 minutes. Stir in the corn and pasta and cook until heated through, 2–3 minutes.

Per serving (generous 2 cups): 416 Cal, 6 g Fat, 2 g Sat Fat, 0 g Trans Fat, 5 mg Chol, 859 mg Sod, 73 g Carb, 9 g Fib, 19 g Prot, 146 mg Calc. *POINTS* value: *8.*

———————————— ● ————————————

TIP Using canned tomatoes with green chiles adds just a bit of heat. Italian-style diced tomatoes could also be used, if you prefer a Mediterranean taste.

6

SPECIAL-OCCASION ENTRÉES

ROMANTIC AND MEMORABLE MEALS

STEAK AU POIVRE

MAKES 2 SERVINGS 🍲 🕐

You can easily make this into an elegant three-course meal: Simply start with sliced boiled new potatoes, topped with caviar and a dab of crème fraîche. Pair the steak with a crisp salad and finish your meal with a poached pear and a scoop of vanilla fat-free frozen yogurt.

2   (3-ounce) beef tenderloin steaks (1½ inches thick), trimmed of all visible fat

¼   teaspoon salt

½   teaspoon cracked black pepper

1   small shallot, finely chopped

2   garlic cloves, minced

¼   cup brandy

¼   cup prepared demi-glace sauce

2   tablespoons Dijon mustard

2   teaspoons unsalted butter

1. Sprinkle the steaks with ⅛ teaspoon of the salt. Press the pepper onto both sides of each steak. Spray a medium nonstick skillet with nonstick spray and set over medium-high heat. Add the steaks and cook, 5–6 minutes on each side for medium-rare. Transfer the steaks to a plate; keep warm.

2. Spray the same skillet with nonstick spray and set over medium-high heat. Add the shallot and garlic; cook, stirring, until fragrant, about 30 seconds. Remove the skillet from the heat and add the brandy. Return the skillet to the heat and cook about 1 minute. Add the demi-glace sauce and mustard; cook, stirring, until the mixture begins to thicken, 2–3 minutes. Remove from the heat, then swirl in the butter and remaining ⅛ teaspoon salt. Pour the sauce over the steaks and serve at once.

Per serving (1 steak with ¼ cup sauce): 238 Cal, 12 g Fat, 5 g Sat Fat, 1 g Trans Fat, 59 mg Chol, 841 mg Sod, 6 g Carb, 1 g Fib, 20 g Prot, 32 mg Calc. *POINTS* value: *6.*

———————————————— • ————————————————

TIP *Demi-glace* is a rich, French brown sauce that takes a while to cook from scratch. Fortunately, you can find prepared *demi-glace* in gourmet stores and in the meat department of some large supermarkets.

Beef Negimaki

MAKES 2 SERVINGS

For an Asian-inspired dinner, start with a comforting bowl of egg drop soup: Simmer reduced-sodium chicken broth, reduced-sodium soy sauce, a little ginger, and some chopped scallions in a saucepan. Then stir in a lightly beaten egg and simmer for a minute. For dessert, cut up some fresh pineapple and orange wedges and serve with one or two almond cookies.

1   (8-ounce) piece of beef round for braciole, trimmed of all visible fat

4   scallions, green part only

1   small garlic clove, minced

1   tablespoon reduced-sodium soy sauce

1   tablespoon seasoned rice vinegar

2   teaspoons Asian (dark) sesame oil

1½ teaspoons honey

1½ tablespoons mirin rice wine

1   tablespoon sake wine

1   cup hot cooked brown rice

1. Cut steak crosswise into 2 equal portions. Arrange steak on a work surface with long side facing you, then top each with 2 of scallions, lengthwise. Roll steaks around scallions, jelly-roll style, and secure with kitchen string at 1-inch intervals. Trim scallions flush with the steaks.

2. Combine the garlic, soy sauce, vinegar, ½ teaspoon of the oil, and the honey in a medium bowl; mix well. Add the steak rolls and toss well to coat; transfer to a zip-close plastic bag and refrigerate at least 4 hours or up to overnight.

3. Remove steak rolls from marinade, reserving marinade. Heat remaining 1½ teaspoons oil in a medium nonstick skillet over medium-high heat. Add the steak rolls and cook, turning every 2 minutes, until cooked though, about 8 minutes. Transfer rolls to a cutting board; cover loosely with foil to keep warm. Add reserved marinade, the mirin, and sake to skillet. Bring to a simmer and cook until flavors are blended, about 30 seconds.

4. Remove the string from the steak rolls. Cut each roll into 6 pieces. Divide the beef negimaki and rice between 2 plates. Spoon the sauce evenly over the negimaki pieces.

Per serving (6 slices negimaki, ½ cup rice, and 1½ tablespoons sauce): 324 Cal, 9 g Fat, 2 g Sat Fat, 0 g Trans Fat, 60 mg Chol, 318 mg Sod, 32 g Carb, 2 g Fib, 26 g Prot, 31 mg Calc. *POINTS* value: *7.*

Wine-Braised Short Ribs

WINE-BRAISED SHORT RIBS

MAKES 4 SERVINGS

It makes sense when cooking a long-braising stew such as this to make enough for leftovers another day. So if it's just the two of you, you can refrigerate the leftover half of the stew for up to three days or freeze for up to one month. It is easily reheated in a saucepan, with a tablespoon or two of water until heated through. Beef short ribs are moderately high in fat so save this recipe for a once-in-a-while treat. Steamed broccoli makes a perfect accompaniment to these ribs.

4	boneless beef short ribs (about 1¼ pounds), trimmed of all visible fat
½	teaspoon salt
¼	teaspoon freshly ground pepper
1	onion, chopped
5	garlic cloves, minced
1	can (15-ounce) Italian-seasoned diced tomatoes
1	cup dry red wine
½	cup reduced-sodium beef broth
3	tablespoons honey
2	tablespoons balsamic vinegar
1	bay leaf

1. Preheat the oven to 300°F.

2. Spray a Dutch oven with nonstick spray and set over medium-high heat. Sprinkle short ribs with ¼ teaspoon of salt and ⅛ teaspoon of pepper and cook until browned, about 4 minutes on each side. Transfer the ribs to a plate.

3. Add the onion and garlic to Dutch oven and cook, stirring, until golden, about 5 minutes. Stir in tomatoes, wine, broth, honey, vinegar, and bay leaf; bring to a boil and cook 3 minutes. Add ribs and the remaining ¼ teaspoon salt and ⅛ teaspoon pepper. Cover and transfer pot to oven. Cook until ribs are fork tender, about 1¾ hours. Let the mixture cool. Discard bay leaf.

4. Refrigerate the rib mixture and sauce 2–3 hours or overnight. Spoon off and discard any congealed fat. Divide ribs and sauce in half; place one half in a container for another time. Transfer other half to a saucepan and simmer until heated through, about 10 minutes.

Per serving (1 short rib and generous ½ cup sauce): 405 Cal, 21 g Fat, 8 g Sat Fat, 1 g Trans Fat, 84 mg Chol, 546 mg Sod, 23 g Carb, 2 g Fib, 29 g Prot, 62 mg Calc. *POINTS* value: *9.*

SAUTÉED VEAL CUTLETS WITH PORT AND DRIED CHERRY SAUCE

MAKES 2 SERVINGS 🍲 ⏱

You might like to start this meal with fresh lump crabmeat sprinkled with lemon juice, served over lettuce, and with prepared cocktail sauce on the side. Finish up your meal with satisfying espresso biscotti.

1 tablespoon all-purpose flour

$\frac{1}{4}$ teaspoon mustard powder

$\frac{1}{4}$ teaspoon dried sage

$\frac{1}{2}$ teaspoon salt

$\frac{1}{2}$ pound veal scaloppini (about 4 cutlets)

2 teaspoons unsalted butter

1 small shallot, finely chopped

$\frac{1}{2}$ cup port wine

$\frac{1}{2}$ cup prepared demi-glace sauce

$\frac{1}{4}$ cup dried tart cherries

$\frac{1}{8}$ teaspoon freshly ground pepper

1. Combine the flour, mustard, sage, and $\frac{1}{4}$ teaspoon of the salt in a bowl. Add the veal and toss to coat. Transfer the veal to a plate.

2. Melt 1 teaspoon of the butter in a nonstick skillet over medium-high heat. Add the veal and cook until lightly browned and cooked through, 2–3 minutes on each side. Transfer the veal to a plate.

3. Add the shallot to the same skillet and cook, stirring, about 30 seconds. Add the port and bring to a boil; cook until reduced by half, 2–3 minutes. Stir in the demi-glace sauce and dried cherries; return to a boil and cook until reduced by half again, 3–4 minutes. Return the veal to the skillet and cook until heated through, about 1 minute. Remove from the heat, then swirl in the remaining 1 teaspoon butter, $\frac{1}{4}$ teaspoon salt, and the pepper.

Per serving (2 veal cutlets and 2 tablespoons sauce): 301 Cal, 10 g Fat, 5 g Sat Fat, 0 g Trans Fat, 86 mg Chol, 912 mg Sod, 28 g Carb, 1 g Fib, 21 g Prot, 50 mg Calc. *POINTS* value: *7.*

———————— • ————————

TIP If you can't find *demi-glace,* use chicken broth.

VEAL WITH LEMON-CAPER SAUCE

MAKES 2 SERVINGS

Make this a romantic three-course meal: For an appetizer, top 2 tomato halves with some seasoned bread crumbs, garlic, and Parmesan cheese then drizzle with a little olive oil. Roast in a hot oven until the tomatoes are heated through. Follow up your meal with fresh berries topped with zabaglione or fat-free nondairy whipped topping.

½ pound veal scaloppini (about 4 cutlets)

½ teaspoon paprika

¼ teaspoon salt

⅛ teaspoon freshly ground pepper

1 tablespoon unsalted butter

3 tablespoons reduced-sodium chicken broth

2 tablespoons fresh lemon juice

2 tablespoons dry white wine

1 tablespoon capers, drained

1 teaspoon dried oregano

1. Working over a sheet of wax paper, sprinkle the veal with the paprika, salt, and pepper.

2. Melt 1 teaspoon of the butter in a nonstick skillet over medium-high heat. Add the veal and cook until lightly browned, about 2 minutes on each side. Add the broth, lemon juice, wine, capers, and oregano; bring to a boil. Reduce the heat and simmer, uncovered, turning the veal once, until the veal is cooked through, about 2 minutes. Remove the skillet from the heat and swirl in the remaining 2 teaspoons butter.

Per serving (2 veal cutlets and 2 tablespoons sauce): 177 Cal, 10 g Fat, 5 g Sat Fat, 1 g Trans Fat, 90 mg Chol, 520 mg Sod, 2 g Carb, 0 g Fib, 18 g Prot, 32 mg Calc. *POINTS* value: *4.*

———————————•———————————

TIP Hearty cooked brown rice (opt for the quick-cooking variety that's ready in 10 minutes) would give a nice contrast to the tangy rich flavors in this dish—½ cup rice will increase your per-serving *POINTS* value by 2. Substitute chicken cutlets for the veal if you prefer.

Garlic Lamb Chops
with Mashed White Beans

GARLIC LAMB CHOPS WITH MASHED WHITE BEANS

MAKES 2 SERVINGS

Lamb is one of the quintessential harbingers of spring. When buying loin lamb chops ask your butcher to trim away all the visible fat to save you time later. Round out your entrée with some fresh steamed greens or roasted asparagus for a true seasonal treat.

4½ garlic cloves, minced

2 teaspoons extra-virgin olive oil

½ teaspoon dried herbes de Provence

¼ teaspoon salt

¼ teaspoon freshly ground pepper

2 (4–5-ounce) loin lamb chops, about ¾-inch thick and trimmed of all visible fat

1 (15½-ounce) can cannellini (white kidney) beans, 2 tablespoons liquid reserved, rinsed and drained

1 tablespoon fresh lemon juice

1 tablespoon chopped fresh parsley

1 teaspoon grated orange zest

1. Combine 3 of the minced garlic cloves, ½ teaspoon of the oil, the herbes de Provence, ⅛ teaspoon of the salt, and ⅛ teaspoon of the pepper in a small bowl. Rub the mixture over the lamb chops; refrigerate, covered, 2 hours or up to overnight.

2. Heat a medium nonstick skillet over medium heat. Add the lamb chops and cook 3–4 minutes on each side for medium-rare. Transfer the chops to a plate and keep warm.

3. Meanwhile, heat the remaining 1½ teaspoons oil in the same skillet over medium heat. Add 1 of the minced garlic cloves and cook until fragrant, about 1 minute. Add the beans and cook, mashing with a wooden spoon until heated through, 2–3 minutes. Remove from the heat and stir in the 2 tablespoons bean liquid, the lemon juice, remaining ⅛ teaspoon salt, and ⅛ teaspoon pepper.

4. Combine the remaining ½ minced garlic clove, the parsley, and orange zest in a small bowl. Sprinkle the lamb chops with the parsley mixture and serve with the beans.

Per serving (1 lamb chop and ½ cup bean mixture): 409 Cal, 13 g Fat, 3 g Sat Fat, 1 g Trans Fat, 74 mg Chol, 729 mg Sod, 38 g Carb, 10 g Fib, 36 g Prot, 69 mg Calc. *POINTS* value: *8.*

MOROCCAN BRAISED PORK WITH DATES AND APRICOTS

MAKES 2 SERVINGS 🍳 ⏲

Start this exotic dinner with a pomegranate-spiked arugula salad with fresh orange sections and a sherry vinaigrette. Serve the pork and couscous with steamed sugar snap peas. Then wrap up your evening with strained fat-free yogurt served with a light sprinkling of toasted walnuts and a drizzle of warm honey.

1   teaspoon extra-virgin olive oil

2   (¼-pound) boneless center-cut pork chops, about ¾-inch thick

½   teaspoon salt

¼   teaspoon freshly ground pepper

1   small onion, chopped

2   garlic cloves, minced

¾   teaspoon ground cumin

¼   teaspoon cinnamon

¼   teaspoon ground ginger

⅛   teaspoon nutmeg

1   cup orange juice

½   cup reduced-sodium chicken broth

1   tablespoon fresh lemon juice

¼   cup pitted dates, sliced

¼   cup dried apricots, sliced

1   cup cooked whole-wheat couscous

1. Heat the oil in a nonstick skillet over medium-high heat. Sprinkle the pork with ¼ teaspoon of the salt and ⅛ teaspoon of the pepper; add to the skillet. Cook the pork until lightly browned, 1–2 minutes on each side. Transfer to a plate and set aside.

2. Add the onion and garlic to the same skillet. Cook, stirring occasionally, until softened, about 2 minutes. Add the cumin, cinnamon, ginger, and nutmeg; cook, stirring constantly, until fragrant, about 30 seconds. Add the orange juice, broth, and lemon juice; bring to a boil and cook until reduced slightly, about 3 minutes. Add the pork; reduce the heat and simmer, covered, until the pork is cooked through, 5–6 minutes.

3. Transfer the pork from the skillet to a plate. Add the dates and apricots to the skillet and boil until the mixture is reduced slightly and the fruit is softened, about 4 minutes. Add the pork and remaining ¼ teaspoon salt and ⅛ teaspoon pepper; cook until heated through, about 1 minute. Serve with the couscous.

Per serving (1 pork chop with ½ cup sauce and ½ cup couscous): 495 Cal, 12 g Fat, 4 g Sat Fat, 0 g Trans Fat, 72 mg Chol, 766 mg Sod, 65 g Carb, 6 g Fib, 33 g Prot, 65 mg Calc. *POINTS value: 10.*

Moroccan Braised Pork with Dates and Apricots

Pork Medallions with Roquefort and Mushrooms

MAKES 2 SERVINGS

Roquefort cheese dates back to Roman times. It is a blue-vein cheese made from sheep's milk and is aged in caves in the Roquefort region of France. It has a creamy texture and pungent, slightly salty flavor. If you can't find it, substitute another good blue-vein cheese such as Stilton or Gorgonzola.

½ pound pork tenderloin, trimmed of all visible fat an cut crosswise into 4 pieces

½ teaspoon salt

¼ teaspoon freshly ground pepper

1 shallot, sliced

2 garlic cloves, sliced

¼ pound fresh white mushrooms, sliced (about 1½ cups)

3 tablespoons Madeira wine

½ cup reduced-sodium chicken broth

1 ounce Roquefort cheese, crumbled

1. Place the pork slices between 2 pieces of wax paper and pound with a wooden mallet or heavy can to a ½-inch thickness.

2. Spray a medium nonstick skillet with nonstick spray and set over medium-high heat. Sprinkle the pork with ¼ teaspoon of the salt and ⅛ teaspoon of the pepper, then add to the skillet. Cook the pork until browned and cooked through, 2–3 minutes on each side. Transfer to a plate and keep warm.

3. Add the shallot, garlic, mushrooms, and remaining ¼ teaspoon salt and ⅛ teaspoon pepper to the skillet. Cook, stirring frequently, until the mushrooms begin to soften, about 3 minutes. Add the wine, scraping up any browned bits from the bottom of the skillet. Cook until the liquid completely evaporates and the mushrooms begin to brown, 3–4 minutes longer. Add the broth and cook about 2 minutes. Add the cheese, reserved pork, and any pork juice on plate; cook, stirring frequently, until the cheese just melts, about 1 minute. Remove the skillet from the heat and serve at once.

Per serving (2 pieces pork, ⅓ cup mushroom mixture): 246 Cal, 9 g Fat, 4 g Sat Fat, 0 g Trans Fat, 82 mg Chol, 965 mg Sod, 7 g Carb, 1 g Fib, 32 g Prot, 102 mg Calc. *POINTS* value: *5.*

JERK CHICKEN THIGHS WITH MANGO SALSA

MAKES 2 SERVINGS 🔥

Much like homemade curries, homemade jerk seasoning can vary from cook to cook. In Jamaica, where "jerked meats" originated, there are both wet marinades and dry rubs. This recipe uses a homemade, wet jerk seasoning marinade. To tame the heat we've substituted a jalapeño pepper for the traditional, extremely hot scotch bonnet chile pepper.

2	scallions, chopped
2	tablespoons fresh lime juice
2	tablespoons chopped fresh cilantro
1	tablespoon reduced-sodium soy sauce
1	tablespoon sugar
1	garlic clove
1	teaspoon grated peeled fresh ginger
1	jalapeño pepper, coarsely chopped (wear gloves to prevent irritation)
3/4	teaspoon ground allspice
1/8	teaspoon nutmeg
2	(6-ounce) skinless bone-in chicken thighs
1	small mango, peeled, pitted, and chopped
2	tablespoons chopped red onion
2	tablespoons orange juice
1/8	teaspoon salt

1. Combine the scallions, lime juice, 1 tablespoon of the cilantro, the soy sauce, sugar, garlic, ginger, jalapeño pepper, allspice, and nutmeg in a blender; puree on high speed. Transfer the mixture to a zip-close plastic bag; add the chicken. Squeeze out the air and seal the bag; turn to coat the chicken. Refrigerate, turning bag occasionally, at least 4 hours or up to overnight.

2. To make the mango salsa, combine the remaining 1 tablespoon cilantro, the mango, onion, orange juice, and salt in a small bowl; set aside.

3. Spray the grill rack with nonstick spray. Prepare the grill. Remove the chicken from the marinade. Grill the chicken 5 inches from the heat, turning frequently, until cooked through, 20–25 minutes. Serve the chicken with the mango salsa.

Per serving (1 chicken thigh and scant 1/2 cup salsa): 296 Cal, 9 g Fat, 3 g Sat Fat, 0 g Trans Fat, 69 mg Chol, 478 mg Sod, 29 g Carb, 3 g Fib, 25 g Prot, 62 mg Calc. *POINTS* value: *6.*

———————————●———————————

TIP You can make the salsa up to a day ahead and keep it, covered, in the refrigerator.

Goat Cheese–Stuffed Chicken Breasts

MAKES 2 SERVINGS

Presentation can make a difference here: Instead of serving the chicken breast rolls whole, cut them into pinwheel slices, arrange them on serving plates and top with the mushroom sauce.

³/₄ cup finely chopped onion

4 garlic cloves, minced

1 teaspoon chopped fresh thyme

6 dried apricots, finely chopped

6 tablespoons sherry wine

1 ounce low-fat goat cheese

2 (¼-pound) skinless boneless chicken breast halves, lightly pounded

¼ teaspoon salt

1 egg white, lightly beaten

½ cup plain dry bread crumbs

1 teaspoon olive oil

¼ pound fresh white mushrooms, sliced

½ cup reduced-sodium chicken broth

⅛ teaspoon freshly ground pepper

1. Preheat oven to 450°F. Spray baking sheet with nonstick spray. Spray a medium nonstick skillet with nonstick spray and set over medium-high heat. Add ½ cup of the onion, 2 of the garlic cloves, and ½ teaspoon of the thyme; cook, stirring until softened, about 2 minutes. Add apricots and 2 tablespoons of sherry; cook until the liquid evaporates, 2–3 minutes. Remove skillet from heat and let cool 2 minutes. Stir in goat cheese and let cool completely.

2. Season chicken with ⅛ teaspoon of salt. Evenly spread goat-cheese mixture on each piece of chicken. Roll up jelly-roll style and secure with wooden picks.

3. Place egg white in a shallow bowl and bread crumbs in another. Dip chicken into egg white then bread crumbs, rolling to coat. Transfer to baking sheet. Lightly spray chicken with nonstick spray and bake until cooked through, 22–25 minutes. Let stand 5 minutes and discard toothpicks.

4. Meanwhile, heat oil in a medium nonstick skillet over medium-high heat. Add remaining ¼ cup onion, 2 garlic cloves, and ½ teaspoon thyme; cook, stirring, until soft, about 1 minute. Stir mushrooms and cook until they give off their liquid, 4–6 minutes. Add the remaining ¼ cup sherry and cook until it is almost evaporated, 1–2 minutes. Add broth, remaining ⅛ teaspoon salt, and the pepper and cook until reduced slightly, about 4 minutes. Serve chicken with mushroom sauce.

Per serving (1 stuffed chicken breast and ⅓ cup sauce): 448 Cal, 11 g Fat, 2 g Sat Fat, 0 g Trans Fat, 30 mg Chol, 800 mg Sod, 48 g Carb, 4 g Fib, 38 g Prot, 135 mg Calc. *POINTS* value: *9*.

Goat Cheese–Stuffed
Chicken Breasts

Coq Au Vin

MAKES 4 SERVINGS

We've made this classic French favorite to serve four so you can serve it to company or enjoy it again another night. If you're saving half for another night, cover and refrigerate it for up to three days or wrap and freeze it for up to two months. A crisp salad of arugula and Belgian endive would complement the rich flavor of the stew.

3   tablespoons all-purpose flour

½   teaspoon salt

¼   teaspoon freshly ground pepper

4   (6-ounce) skinless bone-in chicken thighs

1   tablespoon olive oil

2   slices turkey bacon, chopped

2   cups frozen small white onions, thawed

½   pound fresh white mushrooms, halved

½   pound small red potatoes, scrubbed and quartered

2   carrots, cut into 1½-inch pieces

1   celery stalk, cut into 1½-inch pieces

2   garlic cloves, minced

1   cup dry red wine

½   cup reduced-sodium chicken broth

1   bay leaf

1   teaspoon chopped fresh thyme

1. Combine the flour, salt, and pepper in a medium bowl. Add the chicken and toss to coat. Transfer the chicken to a plate and reserve remaining flour mixture.

2. Heat 2 teaspoons of the oil in a Dutch oven over medium-high heat. Add the chicken and cook until browned, 2–3 minutes on each side. Transfer the chicken to a plate and set aside.

3. Heat the remaining 1 teaspoon oil in the same Dutch oven. Add the bacon and cook, stirring occasionally, about 1 minute. Add the onions, mushrooms, potatoes, carrots, celery, garlic, and the reserved flour mixture; cook, stirring occasionally, until the vegetables begin to soften, 6–7 minutes. Stir in the chicken, wine, broth, bay leaf, and thyme; bring to a boil. Reduce the heat and simmer, covered, until the chicken is cooked through and the vegetables are tender, 25–30 minutes. Discard the bay leaf.

Per serving (1 chicken thigh and 1 cup vegetable mixture): 364 Cal, 14 g Fat, 4 g Sat Fat, 0 g Trans Fat, 73 mg Chol, 544 mg Sod, 28 g Carb, 4 g Fib, 29 g Prot, 68 mg Calc. *POINTS* value: 8.

CHICKEN SCARPARIELLO

MAKES 2 SERVINGS ♦ 🍲

This dish is a staple of most southern Italian restaurants and it is a treat to make at home. To round out the meal, try serving the vegetables over some cooked pasta tossed with a little olive oil and a touch of grated Parmesan cheese. Finish up with fresh sliced strawberries drizzled with a good balsamic vinegar.

2	teaspoons extra-virgin olive oil
2	(¼-pound) skinless boneless chicken thighs
¼	teaspoon salt
⅛	teaspoon freshly ground pepper
1	medium onion, chopped
4	garlic cloves, sliced
1	red bell pepper, seeded and cut into ½-inch pieces
1	jarred hot cherry pepper, seeded and chopped
¼	teaspoon dried oregano
½	cup reduced-sodium chicken broth
¼	cup dry white wine
2	tablespoons chopped fresh parsley

1. Preheat the oven to 400°F.

2. Heat 1 teaspoon of the oil in an ovenproof nonstick skillet or Dutch oven over medium-high heat. Sprinkle the chicken with ⅛ teaspoon of salt and the pepper; add to the skillet and brown, 2 minutes on each side. Transfer the chicken to a plate and set aside.

3. Heat the remaining 1 teaspoon oil in the same skillet. Add the onion, garlic, bell pepper, cherry pepper, and oregano; cook, stirring occasionally, until the vegetables soften, 4–5 minutes. Return the chicken to the skillet; add the broth and wine. Transfer the skillet to the oven and bake until the chicken is cooked through, 12–15 minutes. Remove the skillet from the oven, then stir in the parsley and the remaining ⅛ teaspoon salt.

Per serving (1 chicken thigh and ½ cup vegetables): 290 Cal, 14 g Fat, 4 g Sat Fat, 0 g Trans Fat, 71 mg Chol, 501 mg Sod, 12 g Carb, 3 g Fib, 27 g Prot, 66 mg Calc. *POINTS* value: *6.*

Turkey Pizzaiola

TURKEY PIZZAIOLA

MAKES 2 SERVINGS

Create a delectable three-course meal for your special someone by serving an easy first course of stuffed mussels—cooked mussels on the half-shell, topped with bread crumbs, chopped shallots, olive oil, Parmesan cheese, and herbs. Then wrap it all up with a few spoonfuls of scrumptious tiramisu.

3   ounces whole-wheat linguine

1   teaspoon olive oil

2   (¼-pound) skinless boneless turkey cutlets

⅛   teaspoon salt

    Scant ⅛ teaspoon freshly ground pepper

1   (14½-ounce) can diced tomatoes with balsamic vinegar and olive oil

½   cup dry white wine

2   garlic cloves, minced

1   teaspoon chopped fresh oregano, or ½ teaspoon dried

1   tablespoon grated Parmesan cheese

1. Bring a pot of lightly salted water to a boil. Add the linguine and cook according to package directions.

2. Meanwhile, heat the oil in a nonstick skillet over medium-high heat. Sprinkle the turkey with the salt and pepper and add to the skillet. Cook until the turkey is lightly browned and cooked through, 2–3 minutes on each side. Transfer the turkey to a plate and set aside.

3. Add the tomatoes, wine, garlic, and oregano to the same skillet; bring to a boil. Reduce the heat and simmer until slightly thickened, 4–5 minutes. Return the turkey to the skillet and cook until the turkey is heated though, 1–2 minutes longer. Transfer the turkey cutlets to 2 serving plates; divide the pasta between the plates and top evenly with the sauce. Sprinkle the pasta evenly with the Parmesan cheese and serve at once.

Per serving (1 cutlet, ½ cup pasta, and scant ½ cup sauce): 432 Cal, 10 g Fat, 1 g Sat Fat, 0 g Trans Fat, 77 mg Chol, 1113 mg Sod, 46 g Carb, 5 g Fib, 36 g Prot, 147 mg Calc. *POINTS* value: *9.*

———————————— ● ————————————

TIP   The term *pizzaiola* indicates a sauce made with tomatoes, garlic, and oregano and it is often served over beef and sometimes with a few olives. Here we use lean turkey cutlets instead of beef, but try chicken or veal cutlets if you like.

Pan-Roasted Quail in Port Wine Sauce

MAKES 2 SERVINGS

Quail, an American game bird, is a member of the partridge family. Most quail available today is farm-raised and is suitable to many cooking styles including roasting, broiling, and pan-frying. Look for frozen quail in large supermarket meat departments or ask for it at your local butcher. For information about demi-glace sauce, see page 164.

3/4 cup port wine

2 garlic cloves, crushed

2 tablespoons minced shallots

2 tablespoons sugar

1 tablespoon reduced-sodium soy sauce

1 tablespoon raspberry vinegar

1/4 teaspoon freshly ground pepper

2 (6-ounce) quail, thawed

1/4 teaspoon salt

3/4 cup prepared demi-glace sauce

1 teaspoon chopped fresh thyme

1 teaspoon unsalted butter

1. Combine 1/4 cup of the port, the garlic, 1 tablespoon of the shallots, the sugar, soy sauce, vinegar, and pepper in a zip-close plastic bag; add the quail. Squeeze out the air and seal bag; turn to coat quail. Refrigerate, turning bag occasionally, at least 4 hours or up to overnight.

2. Preheat the oven to 400°F. Spray a baking pan with nonstick spray.

3. Remove the quail from the marinade. Discard the marinade and place the quail in the baking pan. Season the quail with 1/8 teaspoon of the salt. Roast until an instant-read thermometer inserted in the thickest part of the quail registers 180°F, about 23 minutes.

4. Meanwhile, combine the remaining 1/2 cup port and 1 tablespoon shallots with the demi-glace and thyme in a medium saucepan over medium-high heat. Bring to a boil and cook until reduced to 1/2 cup, 12–15 minutes. Strain the sauce through a wire sieve; stir in the butter and the remaining 1/8 teaspoon salt. Serve the sauce with the quail.

Per serving (1 quail and 1/4 cup sauce): 313 Cal, 14 g Fat, 5 g Sat Fat, 0 g Trans Fat, 75 mg Chol, 822 mg Sod, 18 g Carb, 1g Fib, 26 g Prot, 61 mg Calc. *POINTS* value: 7.

EASY PEKING DUCK WRAPS

MAKES 2 SERVINGS

If Peking duck is a favorite of yours, you'll love this easy-to-assemble and easy-to-eat version. Turn it into a party canapé if you like by simply cutting each of the tortillas into four wedges, then topping each with a slice of duck, a spoonful of hoisin sauce, and some of the chopped cucumber and scallion.

4½ tablespoons jarred hoisin sauce

2 tablespoons sake wine

4 teaspoons honey

1 tablespoon reduced-sodium soy sauce

⅛ teaspoon Chinese 5-spice powder

½ pound skinless boneless duck breast

2 (6-inch) fat-free flour tortillas

½ medium cucumber, peeled, seeded, and cut lengthwise into thin slices

1 scallion, green part only, cut in half lengthwise

1. Combine 3 tablespoons of the hoisin sauce, the sake, 3 teaspoons of the honey, the soy sauce, and 5-spice powder in a zip-close plastic bag; add the duck breast. Squeeze out the air and seal the bag; turn to coat the duck. Refrigerate, turning the bag occasionally, at least 4 hours or up to overnight.

2. Combine the remaining 1½ tablespoons hoisin sauce and 1 teaspoon honey in a small bowl; set aside.

3. Preheat the oven to 450°F. Line a 10 x 15-inch jelly roll pan with foil. Stand a wire rack in the pan; lightly spray the rack with nonstick spray.

4. Remove the duck breast from the marinade. Discard the marinade and place the duck on the rack. Bake until the duck is cooked through, 16-18 minutes. Remove the duck from the oven, cover loosely with foil, and let it rest, about 5 minutes.

5. Meanwhile, wrap the tortillas in damp paper towels and microwave on High, 30–60 seconds to warm them. Thinly slice the duck breast across the grain. Spread half of the reserved hoisin-honey mixture over each tortilla. Top each with half of the cucumber, the duck, and then the scallion. Wrap the tortilla around the filling and serve at once.

Per serving (1 wrap): 267 Cal, 2 g Fat, 0 g Sat Fat, 0 g Trans Fat, 66 mg Chol, 664 mg Sod, 34 g Carb, 2 g Fib, 27 g Prot, 67 mg Calc. *POINTS* value: *5.*

CIDER-GLAZED CORNISH HEN

MAKES 2 SERVINGS

Seckel pears are small and russet colored with a sweet-spicy flavor and are excellent for cooking. They are only available in the fall, but you can substitute any other firm, ripe pear, such as Bosc.

$1\frac{1}{2}$ teaspoons olive oil

1 small onion, finely chopped

2 tablespoons finely chopped carrot

1 garlic clove, minced

1 seckel pear, peeled, cored, and chopped (about $\frac{1}{4}$ cup)

2 tablespoons dried cranberries

1 cup cooked basmati rice

$\frac{1}{4}$ cup reduced-sodium chicken broth

$\frac{1}{4}$ teaspoon dried herbes de Provence

$\frac{1}{2}$ teaspoon salt

$\frac{1}{4}$ teaspoon freshly ground pepper

1 cup apple cider

$\frac{1}{4}$ cup maple syrup

$\frac{1}{4}$ teaspoon vanilla extract

$\frac{1}{8}$ teaspoon cinnamon

1 (1-pound) Cornish hen, skin removed

1. Heat 1 teaspoon of oil in a medium nonstick skillet over medium heat. Add the onion, carrot, and garlic; cook, stirring, until softened, 3–4 minutes. Add pear and cranberries; cook 1 minute. Stir in rice, broth, herbes de Provence, $\frac{1}{4}$ teaspoon of salt, and $\frac{1}{8}$ teaspoon of pepper; cook until liquid evaporates, 1–2 minutes. Remove from heat and let mixture cool, about 10 minutes.

2. Combine apple cider and maple syrup in a medium saucepan over medium-high heat. Bring to a boil and cook until mixture is reduced and syrupy, 12–15 minutes. Stir in the vanilla and cinnamon; set aside.

3. Preheat the oven to 450°F. Line a shallow baking pan with foil. Stand a wire rack in the pan; lightly spray the rack with nonstick spray.

4. Loosely stuff hen with rice mixture and secure legs with kitchen twine. Rub hen with remaining $\frac{1}{2}$ teaspoon oil and season with remaining $\frac{1}{4}$ teaspoon salt and $\frac{1}{8}$ teaspoon pepper. Stand hen on rack in pan. Bake 15 minutes. Reduce oven temperature to 400°F. Remove hen from oven; brush with some of cider mixture and continue to roast, brushing every 10 minutes with more cider mixture, until an instant-read thermometer inserted in thickest part of hen registers 180°F, about 45 minutes longer.

Per serving ($\frac{1}{2}$ hen and $\frac{3}{4}$ cup stuffing): 491 Cal, 8 g Fat, 2 g Sat Fat, 0 g Trans Fat, 106 mg Chol, 725 mg Sod, 77 g Carb, 2 g Fib, 27 g Prot, 77 mg Calc. *POINTS* value: *10.*

**Cider-Glazed
Cornish Hen**

Herb-Crusted Salmon
with Tomato Salsa

HERB-CRUSTED SALMON WITH TOMATO SALSA

MAKES 2 SERVINGS ♦ ⊙

Because this is an ideal summertime dish, serve it with a first-course cold soup such as a gazpacho, made from pureed bell pepper, cucumber, onion, and tomato and mixed with some tomato juice and fresh herbs. End the meal with grilled fat-free pound cake brushed with a simple sugar syrup (a tablespoon of sugar dissolved in 2 tablespoons boiling water) flavored with a little grated lime zest and lime juice.

1 tablespoon chopped fresh parsley

1 tablespoon chopped fresh basil

4 teaspoons chopped fresh cilantro

1 large tomato, seeded and finely chopped

1/2 medium jalapeño pepper, seeded and minced (wear gloves to prevent irritation)

2 tablespoons finely chopped red onion

4 teaspoons fresh lime juice

1/4 teaspoon salt

2 (1/4-pound) skin-on salmon fillets

1/8 teaspoon freshly ground pepper

1 tablespoon Dijon mustard

1. Combine the parsley, basil, and 3 teaspoons of the cilantro in a small bowl; transfer to a plate and set aside.

2. Combine the remaining 1 teaspoon cilantro, the tomato, jalapeño pepper, onion, 2 teaspoons of the lime juice, and 1/8 teaspoon of the salt in another bowl.

3. Spray a nonstick ridged grill pan with nonstick spray and set over medium-high heat. Sprinkle the salmon fillets with the remaining 1/8 teaspoon salt and the pepper. Spread the mustard over the flesh sides of the salmon then dip each fillet in the parsley mixture to coat. Place the salmon fillets, flesh-side down, in the grill pan and cook until the salmon is opaque in the center, 5–6 minutes on each side. Serve the salmon with the tomato salsa.

Per serving (1 salmon fillet and 1/2 cup salsa): 197 Cal, 7 g Fat, 2 g Sat Fat, 0 g Trans Fat, 74 mg Chol, 560 mg Sod, 7 g Carb, 2 g Fib, 25 g Prot, 31 mg Calc. *POINTS* value: *4*.

———————— • ————————

TIP Want a special meal for two without too much work on the day you serve it? You can make the salsa up to two days in advance and refrigerate it and you can coat the salmon with the parsley mixture and refrigerate it for up to 24 hours. On the serving day, all you need do is grill the salmon.

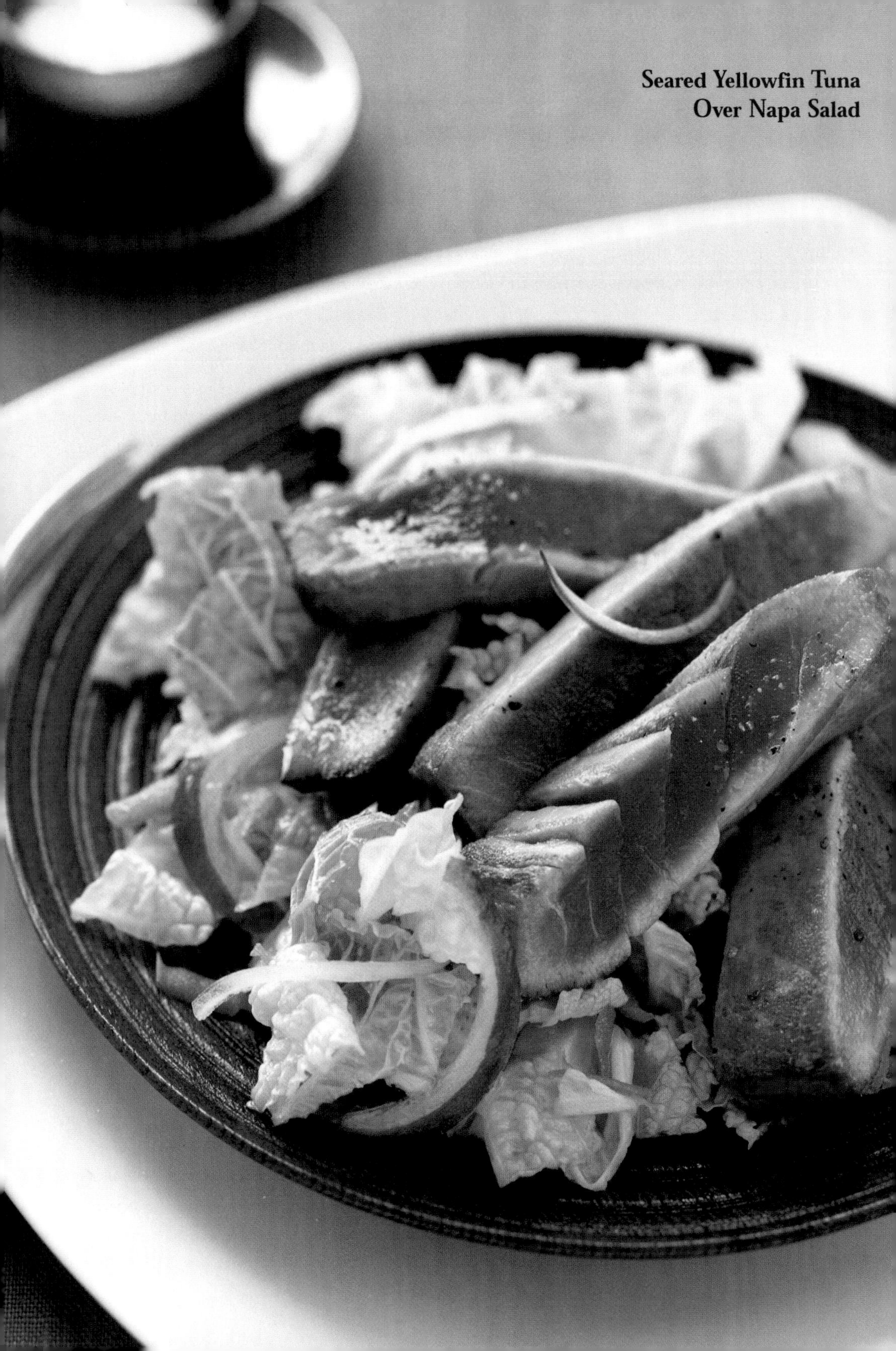
Seared Yellowfin Tuna
Over Napa Salad

SEARED YELLOWFIN TUNA OVER NAPA SALAD

MAKES 2 SERVINGS ⊙

You can complete this Asian-style meal by serving steamed pot stickers (small Chinese dumplings) or dim sum with soy sauce as an appetizer and some sliced pineapple and mango tossed with lime juice and mint for dessert.

2   tablespoons reduced-sodium soy sauce

¹/₂ teaspoon Asian (dark) sesame oil

¹/₈ teaspoon freshly ground pepper

2   (6-ounce) yellowfin tuna steaks, about 1-inch thick

1   tablespoon fresh lemon juice

2   teaspoons honey

1   teaspoon grated peeled fresh ginger

¹/₃ medium head napa cabbage, chopped (about 3 cups)

1   medium carrot, shredded

¹/₂ small red onion, thinly sliced

2   teaspoons peanut oil

2   tablespoons sliced pickled ginger

1. Combine 1 tablespoon of the soy sauce, the sesame oil, and pepper in a zip-close plastic bag; add the tuna. Squeeze out the air and seal the bag; turn to coat the tuna. Let marinate 5 minutes.

2. Meanwhile, combine the remaining 1 tablespoon soy sauce, the lemon juice, honey, and ginger in a large bowl. Add the cabbage, carrot, and onion; toss to coat.

3. Heat the peanut oil in a medium nonstick skillet over medium-high heat. Remove the tuna from the marinade. Discard the marinade and add the tuna to the skillet. Cook the tuna 2–3 minutes on each side for medium-rare. Transfer the tuna to a plate and top each steak with 1 tablespoon of the pickled ginger. Serve with the cabbage salad.

Per serving (1 tuna steak and 1³/₄ cups salad): 280 Cal, 7 g Fat, 1 g Sat Fat, 0 g Trans Fat, 94 mg Chol, 527 mg Sod, 18 g Carb, 6 g Fib, 36 g Prot, 148 mg Calc. *POINTS* value: *5.*

———————————— • ————————————

TIP We give directions for cooking the tuna medium-rare, but if you prefer your tuna medium or well done, simply increase the cooking time. For an additional treat and a touch of heat, serve the tuna with a little wasabi paste mixed with a few drops of lemon juice.

GRILLED HALIBUT WITH LIME-CHIPOTLE BUTTER

MAKES 2 SERVINGS ♦ ☕

Chipotle peppers are dried, smoked jalapeño peppers. They impart both a pleasant smokiness to foods and a fair amount of spiciness or heat. Until recently, dried chipotles could only be found in specialty-food stores and usually in their whole form. A ground, dried form is now widely available in jars in the spice section of your supermarket. Leaving the skin on the fish fillets helps hold the fish together while grilling.

1   tablespoon unsalted butter, softened

1   teaspoon grated lime zest

1   teaspoon chopped fresh cilantro

¼   teaspoon ground chipotle chili powder

¼   teaspoon salt

2   (6-ounce) skin-on halibut fillets

2   teaspoons fresh lime juice

½   teaspoon ground cumin

¼   teaspoon garlic powder

1. Spray the grill rack with nonstick spray. Prepare the grill.
2. Combine the butter, lime zest, cilantro, chipotle pepper, and ⅛ teaspoon of the salt in a small bowl; set aside.
3. Drizzle the halibut fillets with the lime juice. Sprinkle evenly with the cumin, garlic powder, and remaining ⅛ teaspoon salt. Place the fillets, flesh-side down, on the grill and cook until the halibut is opaque in the center, 5–6 minutes on each side. Top each fillet evenly with the chipotle butter and serve at once.

Per serving (1 halibut steak and 2 teaspoons chipotle butter): 184 Cal, 8 g Fat, 4 g Sat Fat, 0 g Trans Fat, 90 mg Chol, 412 mg Sod, 1 g Carb, 0 g Fib, 26 g Prot, 28 mg Calc. *POINTS* value: *4.*

———————————•———————————

TIP Because the lime-chipotle butter works with any number of foods—corn on the cob, chicken breasts or thighs, and filet mignon to name a few—it is great to have on hand. Simply make up a quadruple batch, divide it in fourths, wrap in plastic wrap, and freeze for up to three months.

LOBSTER RISOTTO

MAKES 2 SERVINGS

Risotto is one of Italy's most treasured dishes. The addition of lobster makes this one even more of a special treat and gives it a decidedly American twist. Fresh fennel has a slight taste of anise or licorice. If you like that taste, substitute an equal amount of Pernod (a licorice-flavored liqueur) for the brandy. The feathery green leaves (called fronds) at the top of the fennel also have a slightly anise flavor. You might like to chop a few to add with the basil, just before serving this dish.

3	cups reduced-sodium chicken broth
1	cup water
1 1/2	teaspoons unsalted butter
1/2	small fennel bulb, chopped
1	small shallot, chopped
2	garlic cloves, minced
1/2	cup Arborio rice
3	tablespoons brandy
1/2	pound cooked, shelled lobster meat
2	tablespoons light cream
1/8	teaspoon freshly ground pepper
2	tablespoons fresh basil, thinly sliced

1. Bring the broth and water to a boil in a medium saucepan. Reduce the heat and keep at a simmer.

2. Melt the butter in a medium nonstick skillet over medium heat. Add the fennel, shallot, and garlic; cook, stirring occasionally, until the fennel begins to soften, about 3 minutes. Add the rice and cook, stirring, until the outer shell is translucent, about 1 minute. Add the brandy and cook, stirring, until the liquid is almost completely absorbed.

3. Add 1/2 cup of the hot broth and cook, stirring constantly, until the broth is almost completely absorbed. Continue to add broth, about 1/2 cup at a time, stirring until it is absorbed before adding more, until the rice is just tender. The cooking time should be 18–22 minutes from the first addition of broth. Stir in the lobster meat, cream, and pepper and cook, stirring gently, until the lobster is heated through, about 2 minutes. Remove from the heat and stir in the basil. Serve at once.

Per serving (1 1/2 cups): 436 Cal, 8 g Fat, 3 g Sat Fat, 0 g Trans Fat, 87 mg Chol, 1195 mg Sod, 50 g Carb, 3 g Fib, 36 g Prot, 161 mg Calc. *POINTS* value: *9*.

CITRUS-GINGER SCALLOPS WITH SWEET VEGETABLE SAUTÉ

MAKES 2 SERVINGS

Ginger, lemon, and orange flavors complement the sweet and delicate scallops wonderfully in this recipe. However, if you prefer, you can substitute peeled and deveined large shrimp or cubed tofu for the scallops.

⅓ cup orange juice

2 tablespoons fresh lemon juice

1 tablespoon grated peeled fresh ginger

1 tablespoon reduced-sodium soy sauce

2 teaspoons grated orange zest

4 teaspoons honey

2 garlic cloves, minced

¾ pound sea scallops

1 tablespoon Asian (dark) sesame oil

3 ounces fresh shiitake mushrooms, stems discarded, caps sliced

2 medium carrots, thinly sliced

¼ pound fresh snow peas, trimmed

½ cup frozen peas, thawed

⅓ cup reduced-sodium chicken broth

1. Combine the orange juice, lemon juice, 2 teaspoons of the ginger, the soy sauce, orange zest, honey, and garlic in a large bowl. Add the scallops, tossing to coat; let stand 10 minutes.

2. Using a slotted spoon, transfer the scallops from the marinade to a double layer of paper towels; reserve the marinade and pat the scallops dry.

3. Heat 1 teaspoon of the oil in a large nonstick skillet over medium-high heat. Add the scallops and cook until opaque in the center, 2–3 minutes on each side. Transfer the scallops to a plate.

4. Heat the remaining 2 teaspoons oil in the same skillet. Add the mushrooms, carrots, and remaining 1 teaspoon ginger; cook, stirring occasionally, until the carrots begin to soften. Stir in the snow peas and peas; cook, stirring, about 3 minutes. Add the reserved marinade and the broth; bring to a boil and cook 1 minute. Return the scallops to the skillet and simmer until heated through, about 1 minute longer.

Per serving (1½ cups): 330 Cal, 9 g Fat, 1 g Sat Fat, 0 g Trans Fat, 27 mg Chol, 630 mg Sod, 39 g Carb, 6 g Fib, 26 g Prot, 163 mg Calc. *POINTS* value: 7.

**Citrus-Ginger Scallops with
Sweet Vegetable Sauté**

PAELLA FOR TWO

MAKES 2 SERVINGS

This famous Spanish dish is perfect for a romantic dinner for two. You might like to start with a simple green salad with fat-free balsamic dressing and finish with a creamy-sweet flan. Part of the romance is that traditionally you and your guest serve yourselves right from the pan in which the paella is cooked (a typical paella pan is large with two colorful handles). However, any favorite large skillet or pot would be fine to use here. On a hot summer night, serve the paella with a glass of cold sangria or some chilled fruit nectar.

1 teaspoon extra-virgin olive oil

3 ounces turkey kielbasa, cut into ¼-inch-thick slices

1 medium onion, chopped

3 garlic cloves, minced

1 medium red bell pepper, seeded and chopped

1 medium tomato, seeded and chopped

½ teaspoon saffron threads, lightly crushed

¼ teaspoon dried thyme

1 cup reduced-sodium chicken broth

½ cup long-grain white rice

½ cup frozen peas

10 mussels, scrubbed and debearded

¼ pound large shrimp, peeled and deveined

1. Heat the oil in a paella pan or large nonstick skillet over medium-high heat. Add the kielbasa, onion, garlic, bell pepper, tomato, saffron, and thyme; cook, stirring occasionally, about 5 minutes until the vegetables begin to soften. Add the broth, rice, and peas; bring to a boil. Reduce the heat and simmer, covered, about 10 minutes.
2. Add the mussels and shrimp to the skillet and cover. Increase the heat to medium and cook until the mussels open, the shrimp are opaque in the center, and the rice is cooked, 8–10 minutes longer. Discard any mussels that do not open. Serve the paella at once.

Per serving (about 2 cups): 453 Cal, 9 g Fat, 2 g Sat Fat, 0 g Trans Fat, 102 mg Chol, 993 mg Sod, 60 g Carb, 5 g Fib, 32 g Prot, 108 mg Calc. *POINTS* value: *9.*

BRAISED MUSSELS WITH TOMATO-GARLIC SAUCE

MAKES 2 SERVINGS

If a fra diavolo-style sauce appeals to you, simply step up the heat in this dish by adding $\frac{1}{4}$ teaspoon of crushed red pepper along with the diced tomatoes. The hairy filaments that protrude from a mussel are known as a "beard." To remove, pinch the filaments between thumb and forefinger and pull firmly. Some mussels available today have no beards.

1	tablespoon olive oil
1	medium onion, chopped
4	garlic cloves, minced
1	cup Italian-seasoned diced tomatoes
$\frac{1}{2}$	cup dry white wine
$\frac{1}{4}$	cup chopped fresh basil
2	tablespoons chopped fresh parsley
$1\frac{1}{2}$	pounds mussels, scrubbed and debearded
3	ounces linguine

1. Preheat the oven to 425°F.

2. Heat the oil in a large, ovenproof skillet over medium-high heat. Add the onion and garlic; cook, stirring occasionally, until slightly softened, about 2 minutes. Add the tomatoes; bring to a boil. Reduce the heat and simmer about 2 minutes. Add the wine; bring to a boil. Reduce the heat and simmer about 1 minute. Remove the skillet from the heat and stir in the basil and parsley.

3. Add the mussels to the skillet, spooning the sauce over them. Cover the skillet loosely with foil and place in the oven. Bake until the mussels open, 15–18 minutes. Discard any mussels that do not open.

4. Meanwhile, bring a pot of lightly salted water to a boil. Add the linguine and cook according to package directions; drain. Toss the pasta immediately with about $\frac{1}{2}$ cup of the sauce from the skillet, then turn onto a warm platter. Top with the remaining sauce and mussels and serve at once.

Per serving (1 cup pasta with sauce and 2 cups mussels in shells): 383 Cal, 9 g Fat, 1 g Sat Fat, 0 g Trans Fat, 34 mg Chol, 808 mg Sod, 54 g Carb, 4 g Fib, 21 g Prot, 126 mg Calc. *POINTS* value: *8.*

———————————— • ————————————

TIP Pasta tends to stick together if left to sit after draining for any length of time. To avoid this, toss it immediately with some of the hot sauce.

Crab and
Shrimp Cakes

CRAB AND SHRIMP CAKES

MAKES 4 SERVINGS 🔥

Sriracha is an Asian hot sauce named after Sriracha Harbour, in Thailand. The sauce is made from sun-ripened chiles and has a sweet-tangy spiciness. You can find it in the ethnic-food aisle of some supermarkets and in most Asian markets. As a substitute you can mix a little chile garlic sauce with some ketchup. Mesclun makes a nice bed for serving these fish cakes.

¼ cup low-fat mayonnaise

2 tablespoons chopped fresh cilantro

1 tablespoon fish sauce (nam pla)

2 teaspoons grated peeled fresh ginger

2 teaspoons grated lime zest

1 teaspoon Sriracha hot sauce

6 ounces cooked lump crabmeat, picked over and flaked

¼ pound medium shrimp, peeled, deveined, and chopped

⅔ cup plain dry bread crumbs

1 scallion, chopped

1½ tablespoons peanut oil

Lemon slices, for serving

1. Combine the mayonnaise, cilantro, fish sauce, ginger, lime zest, and Sriracha sauce in a medium bowl. Add the crabmeat, shrimp, ⅓ cup of the bread crumbs and the scallion; mix with a fork until well combined.

2. Spread the remaining ⅓ cup bread crumbs onto a plate. Shape the fish mixture into 4 balls. Roll each ball in the bread crumbs then flatten each into a 3-inch diameter cake.

3. Heat the oil in a large nonstick skillet over medium heat. Add the fish cakes and cook until crisp and golden on the outside and cooked through in the center, about 6 minutes on each side. Serve at once with lemon.

Per serving (1 fish cake): 209 Cal, 8 g Fat, 1 g Sat Fat, 0 g Trans Fat, 69 mg Chol, 650 mg Sod, 20 g Carb, 1 g Fib, 14 g Prot, 97 mg Calc. *POINTS* value: *5.*

———————— • ————————

TIP It seems just as easy to make four of these fish cakes as two, so wrap and refrigerate any leftovers for a cold lunch up to two days later. Or place a fish cake on a plate and microwave on High until heated through, 1–2 minutes and serve warm.

Black Bean-Corn Cakes with Cilantro Sour Cream

MAKES 2 SERVINGS ◊ 🌱

Yellow cornmeal gives a crisp, golden coating to these slightly spicy bean patties. Cilantro sour cream is their refreshing foil. You can substitute plain fat-free yogurt for the sour cream if you like.

1   (10-ounce) can black beans, rinsed, drained, and coarsely mashed

¼   cup shredded reduced-fat sharp cheddar cheese

¼   cup frozen corn, thawed

3   tablespoons yellow cornmeal

2   tablespoons chopped fresh cilantro

1   egg white

1   chipotle en adobo, minced

1   scallion, chopped

1   garlic clove, minced

1½ teaspoons ground cumin

¼   teaspoon salt

1   tablespoon corn oil

¼   cup fat-free sour cream

1   teaspoon grated lime zest

1   teaspoon lime juice

1. Combine the beans, cheese, corn, 1 tablespoon of the cornmeal, 1 tablespoon of the cilantro, the egg white, chipotle pepper, scallion, garlic, cumin, and salt in a medium bowl until well mixed. Divide the mixture into 4 balls.

2. Place the remaining 2 tablespoons cornmeal on a plate. Roll the bean balls in the cornmeal to coat. Press each ball into a ½-inch thick patty.

3. Heat the oil in a large nonstick skillet over medium heat. Add the cakes and cook until crisp and golden outside and heated through, 4–5 minutes on each side. Transfer to a platter; cover with foil to keep warm.

4. To make the cilantro sour cream, combine the sour cream, lime zest, lime juice, and remaining 1 tablespoon cilantro in a small bowl. Serve the bean cakes with the cilantro sour cream.

Per serving (2 bean cakes and 2 tablespoons cilantro cream): 328 Cal, 9 g Fat, 2 g Sat Fat, 0 g Trans Fat, 4 mg Chol, 1046 mg Sod, 45 g Carb, 8 g Fib, 18 g Prot, 263 mg Calc. *POINTS* value: *7.*

———————— • ————————

TIP   These cakes are easy to mix and shape ahead, ready for cooking at the last minute. Simply prepare the recipe through step 2, then wrap and refrigerate for up to three days. Remove the cakes from refrigerator and let stand 5 minutes before proceeding with step 3.

Curried Quinoa with Chickpeas and Almonds

MAKES 2 SERVINGS

Quinoa can be found in most health-food stores and some supermarkets. It is lower in carbohydrates than most grains and higher in protein, with a delicate flavor along the lines of couscous. It is important to rinse quinoa under cold running water before cooking in order to remove its natural bitter coating.

$\frac{1}{2}$ cup quinoa, rinsed

$\frac{1}{2}$ cup orange juice

$\frac{1}{2}$ cup water

$1\frac{1}{2}$ teaspoons curry powder

$\frac{3}{4}$ teaspoon salt

$\frac{1}{2}$ teaspoon ground cumin

$\frac{1}{8}$ teaspoon ground allspice

1 teaspoon olive oil

1 small onion, chopped

1 garlic clove, minced

$\frac{1}{2}$ cup frozen peas and carrots, thawed

$\frac{1}{2}$ (10-ounce) can chickpeas (garbanzo beans), rinsed and drained

2 tablespoons sliced almonds, toasted

$\frac{1}{8}$ teaspoon freshly ground pepper

$\frac{1}{4}$ cup golden raisins

2 scallions, chopped

1 tablespoon chopped fresh cilantro

1 teaspoon grated orange zest

1. Combine the quinoa, orange juice, water, curry powder, $\frac{1}{2}$ teaspoon of the salt, the cumin, and allspice in a medium saucepan; bring to a boil. Reduce the heat and simmer, covered, until the liquid is absorbed, 12–15 minutes.

2. Heat the oil in a nonstick skillet over medium-high heat. Add the onion, garlic, and peas and carrots; cook, stirring frequently, until slightly softened, about 3 minutes. Stir in the chickpeas and almonds; cook, stirring, about 2 minutes longer. Remove the skillet from the heat, then stir in the remaining $\frac{1}{4}$ teaspoon salt and the pepper.

3. Transfer the quinoa mixture to a large bowl. Stir in the raisins, scallions, cilantro, and orange zest; toss well. Stir in the chickpea mixture and serve at once or let the mixture cool to room temperature before serving.

Per serving ($1\frac{1}{3}$ cups): 422 Cal, 10 g Fat, 1 g Sat Fat, 0 g Trans Fat, 0 mg Chol, 110 mg Sod, 75 g Carb, 10 g Fib, 14 g Prot, 126 mg Calc. *POINTS* value: *8.*

VEGETABLE POT PIE

MAKES 2 SERVINGS

Nothing says down-home comfort like pot pie, but unlike traditional pies, this has a healthy, low-fat profile. Serve this satisfying vegetarian entrée with a mixed green salad.

$\frac{1}{4}$ pound small red potatoes, cut into $\frac{1}{4}$-inch dice

1 parsnip, peeled and cut into $\frac{1}{4}$-inch pieces

$1\frac{1}{2}$ teaspoons unsalted butter

1 small onion, chopped

2 garlic cloves, minced

$\frac{3}{4}$ teaspoon dried basil

$\frac{1}{4}$ teaspoon dried thyme

$\frac{1}{2}$ cup frozen peas and carrots

1 ($10\frac{1}{2}$-ounce) can red kidney beans, rinsed and drained

$\frac{1}{2}$ tablespoon cornstarch

$1\frac{1}{2}$ cups low-fat (1%) milk

2 teaspoons Dijon mustard

$\frac{1}{2}$ teaspoon salt

$\frac{1}{8}$ teaspoon freshly ground pepper

2 (12 x 17-inch) sheets phyllo dough, thawed according to package directions

1. Preheat the oven to 400°F. Spray a 1-quart baking dish with nonstick spray. Bring the potatoes with enough water to cover to a boil in a large saucepan. Reduce the heat and simmer 6 minutes. Add the parsnip and simmer 2 minutes; drain.

2. Melt butter in nonstick skillet over medium-high heat. Add onion, garlic, basil, and thyme; cook, stirring occasionally, until onion softens, about 4 minutes. Add parcooked potatoes and parsnip, and the peas and carrots; cook, stirring frequently, until softened, about 2 minutes. Add kidney beans and cook, stirring, about 1 minute longer.

3. Combine the cornstarch and $\frac{1}{2}$ cup of the milk in a bowl until blended; stir in the remaining 1 cup milk, the mustard, salt, and pepper. Add the milk mixture to the skillet and cook, stirring constantly, until the mixture just comes to a simmer and thickens, about 3 minutes. Transfer the mixture to the baking dish.

4. Place 1 phyllo sheet on a work surface; spray lightly with nonstick spray then fold in half, short side to short side. Lightly spray the top with nonstick spray. Set the sheet, sprayed-side up, over the baking dish letting any extra drape over the sides. Repeat with remaining phyllo sheet. Carefully roll and tuck the overhanging phyllo under. Bake until the top is golden and the filling is bubbling and thick, about 20 minutes. Let stand 5 minutes before serving.

Per serving ($\frac{1}{2}$ of pot pie): 451 Cal, 7 g Fat, 3 g Sat Fat, 0 g Trans Fat, 23 mg Chol, 1165 mg Sod, 79 g Carb, 12 g Fib, 20 g Prot, 313 mg Calc. *POINTS* value: *9.*

Vegetable Pot Pie

LENTILS WITH WINE-BRAISED VEGETABLES

MAKES 2 SERVINGS 🥕

French lentils, also called *Puy* lentils, are green and can be found in gourmet markets, health-food stores, and some large supermarkets. They have more flavor and hold their shape better than common brown lentils. If you can't find French lentils, brown will work fine here, too. You can serve each portion of lentils with ½ cup cooked pasta such as farfalle and increase the per-serving *POINTS* value by 2.

3	cups water
½	cups French lentils, picked over and rinsed
2	sprigs fresh thyme, or ½ teaspoon dried
¾	teaspoon salt
1	tablespoon extra-virgin olive oil
1	onion, chopped
2	carrots, cut into ½-inch pieces
2	shallots, peeled and chopped
2	garlic cloves, sliced
1	celery stalk, cut into ½-inch pieces
⅔	cup dry red wine
3	tablespoons tomato paste
1	cup reduced-sodium vegetable broth
2	tablespoons fresh basil leaves, thinly sliced
⅛	teaspoon freshly ground pepper

1. Bring the water, lentils, thyme, and ½ teaspoon of the salt to a boil in a large saucepan. Reduce the heat and simmer, uncovered, until the lentils are tender but hold their shape, about 23 minutes. Drain the lentils and set aside.

2. Heat the oil in a large nonstick skillet over medium-high heat. Add the onion, carrots, shallots, garlic, and celery; cook, stirring occasionally, until lightly browned, about 6 minutes. Add the wine and tomato paste; bring to a boil. Reduce the heat and simmer until the liquid reduces and thickens slightly, about 3 minutes. Add the broth, simmer until reduced by half, about 8 minutes. Stir in the lentils, basil, remaining ¼ teaspoon salt, and the pepper; cook until heated through.

Per serving (about 1 cup): 331 Cal, 8 g Fat, 1 g Sat Fat, 0 g Trans Fat, 0 mg Chol, 741 mg Sod, 48 g Carb, 15 g Fib, 18 g Prot, 97 mg Calc. *POINTS* value: *6.*

TOFU AND SNOW PEA STIR-FRY

MAKES 2 SERVINGS

Tofu is a great heart-healthy source of protein. Be sure to use the firm or extra-firm variety in this recipe; soft or silken tofu would fall apart too easily here. To complete this simple dish, you can serve it with ½ cup cooked brown or white rice (the per-serving *POINTS* value will increase by 2).

¼   cup hoisin sauce

2   tablespoons dry sherry wine

2   tablespoons mirin rice wine

1   tablespoon rice vinegar

1   tablespoon honey

8   ounces low-fat firm tofu,
    pressed and cut crosswise
    into 4 slices

2   teaspoons Asian (dark)
    sesame oil

2   garlic cloves, minced

2   teaspoons grated peeled
    fresh ginger

¼   pound fresh snow peas,
    trimmed

4   scallions, cut into ½-inch pieces

1. Combine the hoisin sauce, sherry, mirin, vinegar, and honey in a shallow dish. Add the tofu slices, turning to coat; let stand 30 minutes turning occasionally.

2. Heat 1 teaspoon of the oil in a nonstick skillet over medium-high heat. Lift the tofu from the marinade (reserve the marinade) and add the tofu to the skillet. Cook until golden, about 2 minutes on each side. Transfer the tofu to 2 serving plates; keep warm.

3. Heat the remaining 1 teaspoon oil in the same skillet. Add the garlic and ginger; stir-fry until fragrant, about 30 seconds. Add the snow peas and stir-fry, about 1 minute. Add the scallions and stir-fry 1 minute longer. Add the reserved marinade and cook until hot, about 30 seconds. Pour the vegetables and sauce evenly over the tofu and serve at once.

Per serving (2 slices tofu, ¾ cup vegetables and sauce): 326 Cal, 13 g Fat, 2 g Sat Fat, 0 g Trans Fat, 0 mg Chol, 529 mg Sod, 39 g Carb, 8 g Fib, 17 g Prot, 155 mg Calc. *POINTS* value: *7.*

TIP   For this recipe it is important to press the tofu to rid it of excess water. To press tofu, place it between 2 plates then place a weight, such as a heavy can, on top. Let it stand until it expels some of its liquid, about 25 minutes. Drain off the liquid and pat the tofu dry with paper towels.

Wild Mushroom Ravioli in Simple Tomato Sauce

WILD MUSHROOM RAVIOLI IN SIMPLE TOMATO SAUCE

MAKES 2 SERVINGS

Wonton wrappers (sometimes called wonton skins) make wonderful ravioli. Frozen wonton wrappers can be found in the ethnic section of the frozen food department in many supermarkets.

1	tablespoon extra-virgin olive oil
$\frac{1}{4}$	pound fresh shiitake mushrooms, stems discarded, caps very thinly sliced
1	small onion, finely chopped (about 5 tablespoons)
4	garlic cloves, minced
$\frac{1}{2}$	cup dry white wine
$\frac{1}{2}$	teaspoon salt
$\frac{1}{4}$	teaspoon freshly ground pepper
10	wonton wrappers, thawed if frozen
$\frac{3}{4}$	pound plum tomatoes, cored, seeded, and chopped
2	tablespoons tomato paste
1	tablespoon chopped fresh basil
2	tablespoons freshly grated Parmigiano-Reggiano cheese

1. Heat 2 teaspoons of oil in a nonstick skillet over medium-high heat. Add mushrooms, 1 tablespoon of onion, and 2 of garlic cloves; cook, stirring occasionally, until softened, about 3 minutes. Add $\frac{1}{4}$ cup of wine, simmer until liquid evaporates and mushrooms are light golden, about 8 minutes. Stir in $\frac{1}{4}$ teaspoon of salt and $\frac{1}{8}$ teaspoon of pepper. Remove skillet from heat and let cool completely.

2. Arrange 5 of wonton wrappers on work surface. Place 2 teaspoons mushroom mixture in center of each. Moisten edge of wrappers with water and fold $\frac{1}{2}$ of wrapper over filling; press edges to seal and form a triangle. Repeat with remaining wrappers and filling, making a total of 10 ravioli. Place ravioli on a baking sheet and cover with damp paper towels.

3. Heat remaining 1 teaspoon oil in large nonstick skillet over medium-high heat. Add remaining $\frac{1}{4}$ cup onion and 2 garlic cloves; cook, stirring, about 2 minutes. Add remaining $\frac{1}{4}$ cup wine, the tomatoes, and tomato paste; bring to a simmer and cook until slightly thickened, about 3 minutes. Remove from heat then stir in basil, remaining $\frac{1}{4}$ teaspoon salt and $\frac{1}{8}$ teaspoon pepper. Cover to keep hot.

4. Bring a large saucepan of lightly salted water to a simmer. Add the ravioli and simmer (do not let them boil) about 5 minutes. Remove with a slotted spoon, let drain, and place in 2 serving bowls. Top each bowl evenly with the sauce and cheese.

Per serving (5 ravioli with $\frac{1}{3}$ cup sauce and 1 tablespoon cheese): 296 Cal, 10 g Fat, 2 g Sat Fat, 0 g Trans Fat, 26 mg Chol, 881 mg Sod, 42 g Carb, 5 g Fib, 10 g Prot, 133 mg Calc. *POINTS* value: *6.*

7

Sweets for the Sweet

DESSERTS—FROM SIMPLE TO INDULGENT

CARAMEL-PECAN BAKED APPLES

MAKES 2 SERVINGS

You might like to serve these at Halloween. They're good for adults and kids, giving them something sweet and delicious (other than candy) to enjoy. If you like, use dried cranberries instead of raisins and dress up the apples by garnishing each one with a cinnamon stick. Northern Spy, Cortland, and McIntosh apples would make suitable alternatives to Rome apples. Look for fresh apples in farmers' markets and at roadside stands in the fall.

1 tablespoon chopped dates

1 tablespoon coarsely chopped dark raisins

1 tablespoon coarsely chopped pecans

1 tablespoon packed brown sugar

¼ teaspoon cinnamon

⅛ teaspoon nutmeg

2 large Rome apples

1 teaspoon cold butter, cut into small pieces

2 tablespoons jarred fat-free caramel sauce

1. Preheat the oven to 375°F. Pour ¼ cup water into an 8-inch square baking dish.

2. Toss together the dates, raisins, pecans, brown sugar, cinnamon, and nutmeg in a small bowl. Core the apples with a small knife, but do not cut all the way through to the bottoms. Peel about ½ inch of skin from the tops of the apples. Fill the apples with the date mixture; stand in the baking dish and dot the filling with the butter.

3. Cover the apples loosely with a foil tent and bake, basting the apples occasionally with the pan juices, until almost tender, about 40 minutes. Uncover and bake until the apples are tender, about 15 minutes longer.

4. Transfer the apples to dessert plates with a slotted spoon. Drizzle with the caramel sauce.

Per serving (1 baked apple and 1 tablespoon caramel sauce): 277 Cal, 5 g Fat, 2 g Sat Fat, 0 g Trans Fat, 5 mg Chol, 88 mg Sod, 61 g Carb, 7 g Fib, 1 g Prot, 43 mg Calc. *POINTS* value: *5.*

TIP These apples are easily made in the microwave. Simply place the stuffed apples in a small microwavable baking dish. Pour ¼ cup water around the apples and microwave, covered, on High, 7 to 10 minutes. Let the apples stand 5 minutes before serving.

Caramel-Pecan Baked Apples

Spiced Pear Pouches

MAKES 2 SERVINGS

Phyllo dough, available in supermarkets everywhere, keeps the *POINTS* value low and the flavor high in this easy and elegant dessert. Phyllo, the Greek word for "leaf," is used in classic Middle Eastern dishes, including baklava (honey and nut pastries) and spanakopita (spinach pie). Unopened, phyllo dough can be frozen for up to six months or refrigerated for up to one month. The best way to thaw it is overnight in the refrigerator, but if you are careful, it can also be gently thawed in the microwave on Low, checking it every 30 seconds or so.

1   large ripe pear, such as Bartlett, Anjou, or Bosc, peeled, cored, and cut into ¼-inch dice

1   tablespoon + 1 teaspoon sugar

1   teaspoon all-purpose flour

1   teaspoon currants

½   teaspoon cinnamon

½   teaspoon fresh lemon juice

2   (12 x 17-inch) sheets phyllo dough, at room temperature

2   teaspoons chopped pecans

1. Preheat the oven to 375°F. Spray 2 (8-ounce) custard cups with nonstick spray.

2. Toss together the pear, 1 tablespoon of the sugar, the flour, currants, cinnamon, and lemon juice in a small bowl; set aside.

3. Place 1 phyllo sheet on a clean, dry work surface. (As you work, keep the remaining sheet of phyllo covered to keep it from drying out.) Lightly spray the phyllo with nonstick spray, then cut into 4 rectangles. Stack the rectangles on top of each other. Repeat with remaining phyllo sheet making a total of 2 stacks. Gently ease each stack into a custard cup, pressing the phyllo against the bottoms of the cups. Spoon the pear mixture into the cups and sprinkle with the pecans. Gather the edges of the phyllo so they slightly cover the pears. Lightly spray the phyllo with nonstick spray and sprinkle with the remaining 1 teaspoon sugar.

4. Bake until the phyllo is golden and the pear mixture is bubbling, about 25 minutes. Serve warm.

Per serving (1 pouch): 168 Cal, 3 g Fat, 0 g Sat Fat, 0 g Trans Fat, 0 mg Chol, 43 mg Sod, 35 g Carb, 3 g Fib, 2 g Prot, 23 mg Calc. *POINTS* value: *3*

PLUM-ALMOND CRISP

MAKES 2 SERVINGS

If you happen to have old-fashioned rolled oats in your pantry, use them instead of quick-cooking oats. They will add a bit more texture to the topping. You can substitute hazelnuts for almonds and, for the most flavor, toast the nuts before adding them to the topping mixture.

4	medium plums, halved, pitted, and cut into $1/2$-inch-thick slices
3	tablespoons sugar
$1/2$	teaspoon fresh lemon juice
$1/4$	teaspoon cinnamon
$1/8$	teaspoon salt
2	tablespoons quick-cooking rolled oats
1	tablespoon all-purpose flour
1	tablespoon sliced almonds, coarsely chopped
1	teaspoon butter, melted

1. Preheat the oven to 375°F. Spray 2 (6-ounce) custard cups with nonstick spray.

2. Combine the plums, 2 tablespoons of the sugar, the lemon juice, cinnamon, and salt in a medium bowl. Divide the plum mixture between the custard cups.

3. Combine the oats, flour, almonds, the remaining 1 tablespoon sugar, and the melted butter in a small bowl until crumbs form. Sprinkle the oat mixture evenly over the plum mixture then lightly spray with nonstick spray.

4. Place the custard cups on a small baking sheet. Bake the crisps until the filling is bubbling and the top is golden, 25–30 minutes.

Per serving (1 crisp): 219 Cal, 5 g Fat, 2 g Sat Fat, 0 g Trans Fat, 5 mg Chol, 155 mg Sod, 43 g Carb, 3 g Fib, 3 g Prot, 20 mg Calc. *POINTS* value: *4*.

Blueberry Cobblers

BLUEBERRY COBBLERS

MAKES 2 SERVINGS

Crisps, cobblers, grunts, betties, pandowdies, and buckles are old-fashioned desserts that contain fruit and a dough-like topping. Biscuits, bread crumbs, pastry dough, crumb mixtures, and batters are just some of the toppings that define these regional specialties. Their homey quality and ease of preparation has made them American classics. Our individual cobblers, redolent with fresh ginger and lemon peel, are the perfect ending for a romantic dinner for two.

1½ cups fresh blueberries

2 tablespoons + ½ teaspoon sugar

1 teaspoon minced peeled fresh ginger

1 teaspoon grated lemon zest

1 teaspoon fresh lemon juice

¼ teaspoon cinnamon

½ cup reduced-fat baking mix

3 tablespoons fat-free milk

1. Preheat the oven to 400°F. Spray 2 (6-ounce) custard cups with nonstick spray.
2. Combine the blueberries, 2 tablespoons of the sugar, the ginger, lemon zest, lemon juice, and cinnamon in a medium bowl. Divide the blueberry mixture between the custard cups.
3. Combine the baking mix and milk in a small bowl. Spoon the batter over the blueberry mixture and sprinkle with the remaining ½ teaspoon sugar. Place the custard cups on a small baking sheet.
4. Bake the cobblers until the topping is golden and the filling is bubbling, about 20 minutes. Serve warm or at room temperature.

Per serving (1 cobbler): 237 Cal, 3 g Fat, 1 g Sat Fat, 0 g Trans Fat, 0 mg Chol, 348 mg Sod, 51 g Carb, 4 g Fib, 4 g Prot, 65 mg Calc. *POINTS* value: *4.*

———————————— • ————————————

TIP You can make the cobblers early in the day to serve at room temperature or reheat them in a 375°F oven for 10 to 12 minutes to serve warm. Frozen blueberries can be used in place of fresh berries: They do not need to be thawed.

Balsamic Berries 'n Cream

MAKES 2 SERVINGS ⏱

When it comes to balsamic vinegar, buy the best your pocketbook will allow. Balsamic vinegar can range in price from a mere $3 to well over $100 a bottle. Authentic balsamic vinegar has been produced in the Italian provinces of Modena and Reggio for almost 1000 years. To know what you are getting, read the label carefully. The best vinegars have Aceto Balsamico Tradizionale di Modena on the label. To enrich the flavor of moderately-priced balsamic vinegar, we cook it with a little sugar, which helps balance its flavor. You will find that as the tangy glaze cools it will thicken. If the glaze becomes too thick to drizzle, add about ½ teaspoon water to thin it slightly. Drizzle over a slice of angel food cake that is topped with berries, sprinkle it over string beans or asparagus, or brush a little over salmon before broiling or baking it.

½   cup balsamic vinegar

2   tablespoons sugar

¼   teaspoon cinnamon

⅛   teaspoon ground allspice

¼   cup sliced fresh strawberries

¼   cup fresh raspberries

¼   cup fresh blueberries

1   teaspoon maple syrup

1   cup low-fat vanilla ice cream or frozen yogurt

1. Bring the vinegar, sugar, cinnamon, and allspice to a boil in a medium saucepan. Boil until the mixture is reduced to a syrupy glaze, about 5 minutes (you should have about 2 tablespoons glaze); set aside.

2. Combine the strawberries, raspberries, blueberries, and maple syrup in a small bowl. Place a ½-cup scoop of the ice cream in each of 2 small bowls; top with the berry mixture and drizzle with the glaze. Serve at once.

Per serving (½ cup ice cream, ⅓ cup berries, and 1 tablespoon glaze): 218 Cal, 5 g Fat, 3 g Sat Fat, 0 g Trans Fat, 19 mg Chol, 57 mg Sod, 44 g Carb, 2 g Fib, 3 g Prot, 105 mg Calc. *POINTS* value: *4.*

Orange-Scented Rice Pudding

MAKES 2 SERVINGS

A delicious rice pudding is a great way to use up leftover rice. This pudding can be eaten warm or chilled and can be spiced up with a light sprinkling of ground cinnamon. For a flavorful warm-weather variation, make rice pudding parfaits by spooning alternating layers of rice pudding and cut-up fruit or berries into parfait glasses or goblets.

1	cup fat-free milk
1	cup cooked long-grain white rice
¼	cup dark raisins
1	tablespoon sugar
1	teaspoon grated orange zest
¼	teaspoon vanilla extract

1. Bring the milk, rice, raisins, and sugar to a boil in a medium saucepan. Reduce the heat and simmer, uncovered, stirring often, until the pudding is thick and creamy, about 15 minutes.

2. Remove the pudding from the heat and stir in the orange zest and vanilla. Let stand at room temperature to cool slightly, then serve warm or cover and refrigerate until chilled, about 2 hours.

Per serving (generous ½ cup): 230 Cal, 1 g Fat, 0 g Sat Fat, 0 g Trans Fat, 2 mg Chol, 66 mg Sod, 50 g Carb, 1 g Fib, 7 g Prot, 169 mg Calc. *POINTS* value: *4.*

White Chocolate Soufflés

MAKES 4 SERVINGS

This impressive yet easy-to-prepare recipe can be doubled or tripled for entertaining. Coat the ramekins and prepare the white chocolate base up to four hours ahead of time. Be sure to press plastic wrap directly against the surface of the chocolate base to prevent a skin from forming, then refrigerate it. When you are about 30 minutes from sitting down to dessert, preheat the oven and proceed from step 3. Leftovers (though they won't be puffed) are delicious cold.

3   teaspoons sugar

2   (1-ounce) squares white baking chocolate, coarsely chopped

1   tablespoon fat-free milk

1   egg yolk

1   tablespoon all-purpose flour

2   egg whites

¼   teaspoon cream of tartar

1. Preheat the oven to 400°F. Spray 4 (4-ounce) ramekins with nonstick spray. Sprinkle 1 teaspoon of the sugar into one of the cups, turning the cup to coat the bottom and side with the sugar. Pour the excess sugar into the second ramekin and repeat to coat with the sugar. Repeat with the remaining cups. Refrigerate the sugared cups until ready to use.

2. Place chocolate and milk in a medium microwavable bowl. Microwave on High about 30 seconds, stirring at 10-second intervals, until the chocolate is melted and smooth. Whisk in the egg yolk and flour until blended and smooth; set aside until cool, 6–8 minutes.

3. With an electric mixer on medium speed, beat the egg whites and cream of tartar in a medium bowl until soft peaks form, 1–2 minutes. Sprinkle with the remaining 2 teaspoons sugar and beat until soft, glossy peaks form, about 2 minutes longer. Gently fold the beaten egg whites into the chocolate mixture.

4. Spoon the chocolate mixture into the ramekins. Place the filled cups on a small baking sheet. Bake until puffed and golden, 10–15 minutes. Serve at once.

Per serving (1 soufflé): 118 Cal, 9 g Fat, 5 g Sat Fat, 0 g Trans Fat, 53 mg Chol, 34 mg Sod, 9 g Carb, 2 g Fib, 4 g Prot, 22 mg Calc. *POINTS* value: *3.*

Rum Custard

MAKES 2 SERVINGS

Custard is comfort food at its best. Some custards are slowly simmered on top of the stove, while others are baked in a water bath so they will set up slowly, assuring the silky-smooth texture we have come to expect of a well-made custard. Custards can be made with cream, half-and-half, or milk and are thickened with whole eggs or a combination of yolks and eggs. It simply depends upon how rich or light the custard is meant to be. Here, it is flavored with dark rum and nutmeg, but you could add a splash of pure vanilla extract, if you like.

1   large egg

2   tablespoons sugar

Pinch salt

¾   cup low-fat (1%) milk

1   tablespoon dark rum

⅛   teaspoon nutmeg

1. Preheat the oven to 350°F. Spray 2 (6-ounce) custard cups with nonstick spray.

2. Whisk together the egg, sugar, and salt in a medium bowl; set aside.

3. Bring the milk to a boil in a small saucepan. Remove the saucepan from the heat and stir in the rum and nutmeg. Slowly whisk the milk mixture into the egg mixture until blended. Pour the custard mixture into the custard cups. Place the cups in an 8-inch square baking pan. Fill the pan with hot tap water to come halfway up the sides of the custard cups.

4. Bake until a knife inserted in the center of a custard comes out clean, 30–40 minutes. Cool the custards on a rack 15 minutes. Cover and refrigerate until set, at least 4 hours or overnight.

Per serving (1 custard): 142 Cal, 4 g Fat, 1 g Sat Fat, 0 g Trans Fat, 110 mg Chol, 219 mg Sod, 17 g Carb, 0 g Fib, 6 g Prot, 126 mg Calc. *POINTS* **value:** *3.*

CHOCOLATE SEMIFREDDO

MAKES 2 SERVINGS ✖

A popular Italian dessert, semifreddo, which means "half-cold," most often refers to mousse-like desserts that have bits of chocolate, crumbled cookies, chopped nuts, or fruit folded in, then frozen. These airy concoctions never freeze hard, however, which makes their texture especially pleasing to the palate. Some semifreddos are refrigerated—not frozen—like our silky smooth, no-cook version, which is made with sweetened whipped ricotta cheese. Its enticing taste is reminiscent of the filling used in another Italian favorite—cannoli.

1 cup fat-free ricotta cheese

4 teaspoons confectioners' sugar

½ teaspoon vanilla extract

2 tablespoons semisweet chocolate chips, melted

¼ cup fat-free nondairy whipped topping

Puree the ricotta cheese, confectioners' sugar, and vanilla in a food processor. Scrape into a medium bowl. Stir in the melted chocolate until well mixed. With a rubber spatula, gently fold in the whipping topping until blended. Cover and refrigerate until well chilled, at least 1 hour. Spoon into goblets or dessert dishes to serve.

Per serving (generous ½ cup): 192 Cal, 5 g Fat, 3 g Sat Fat, 0 g Trans Fat, 12 mg Chol, 100 mg Sod, 22 g Carb, 1 g Fib, 17 g Prot, 208 mg Calc. *POINTS* value: *4.*

———————— • ————————

TIP To melt the chocolate chips, microwave in a small microwavable bowl on High, 20 to 25 seconds, stirring at 10-second intervals, until melted and smooth. Or, to melt on the stove, place the chocolate in the top of a double-boiler set over barely simmering water. Stir until melted and smooth, 1 to 2 minutes.

Chocolate Semifreddo

APRICOT FOOL

MAKES 2 SERVINGS

An old-fashioned English dessert, a fool is cooked fruit puree that is combined with whipped cream. The cream and fruit are usually gently folded together in a clear glass bowl to create an appealing swirled effect. Originally, fools were always made with gooseberries, but nowadays almost any berry will do. The fruit puree can be made up to several days ahead for ease of preparation. And, if you like, top the finished desserts with crushed gingersnap cookies (2 cookies will increase the *POINTS* value by 1).

1½ cups water

½ cup dried apricots

1 tablespoon sugar

⅛ teaspoon almond extract

¼ cup light nondairy whipped topping

1. Bring the water, apricots, and sugar to a boil in a medium saucepan. Reduce the heat and simmer, covered, stirring occasionally, until the apricots soften, about 10 minutes. Remove from the heat and stir in the almond extract.

2. Puree the apricot mixture in a food processor or blender. Transfer the puree to a medium bowl. Gently fold in the whipped topping with a rubber spatula until blended. Cover and refrigerate at least 1 hour before serving. To serve, spoon into goblets or dessert dishes.

Per serving (½ cup): 120 Cal, 1 g Fat, 1 g Sat Fat, 0 g Trans Fat, 0 mg Chol, 9 mg Sod, 28 g Carb, 3 g Fib, 1 g Prot, 20 mg Calc. *POINTS* value: *2.*

TIP To quickly cool down the cooked fruit puree, try this chef's trick—place a bowl of the fruit puree into a larger bowl filled halfway with water and plenty of ice; let stand until cool, stirring occasionally, about 15 minutes.

GINGERED PEACH CRÊPES

MAKES 2 SERVINGS ✖ ⏱

Just about every country has their version of pancakes. The French call them crêpes, in Hungary they are called palacsinta, in China they are called Peking doilies and moo shu pancakes, our Jewish friends call them blintzes, and in Italy, delicate crespelle are used to make cannelloni. Crêpes can be sweet or savory and can be served as an appetizer or snack, main course for lunch, brunch, or breakfast, or be the simple ending or the grand finale to a dinner.

2   ripe peaches (about ¾ pound), halved, pitted, and chopped

2   tablespoons granulated sugar

1   tablespoon chopped candied ginger

1   teaspoon fresh lemon juice

2   tablespoons light nondairy whipped topping

2   (7-inch) ready-to-use crêpes (part of a 4.5-ounce package)

1   teaspoon confectioners' sugar

1. Combine the peaches, granulated sugar, ginger, and lemon juice in a medium bowl; let stand 10 minutes.

2. Place ½ of the peach mixture and 1 tablespoon of the whipped topping in the center of each crêpe; roll up to enclose the filling. Place the filled crêpes, seam-side down, on dessert plates. Sprinkle with confectioners' sugar.

Per serving (1 crêpe): 232 Cal, 4 g Fat, 2 g Sat Fat, 1 g Trans Fat, 38 mg Chol, 189 mg Sod, 45 g Carb, 3 g Fib, 5 g Prot, 80 mg Calc. *POINTS* value: *4*.

———————— • ————————

TIP Place the confectioners' sugar in a small sieve or tea strainer to lightly dust the crêpes.

Bananas Foster Parfaits

BANANAS FOSTER PARFAITS

MAKES 2 SERVINGS

According to John Mariani in *The Dictionary of American Food and Drink,* Bananas Foster was created at Brennan's restaurant in New Orleans in the 1950s as part of a Breakfast at Brennan's promotion. It was named after Mr. Foster, who happened to be one of their regular customers. Here, all of the delicious elements of this popular dessert have been turned into a mouth-watering parfait that will carry you to New Orleans with every mouthful.

½ (1-ounce) package sugar-free instant vanilla pudding (about 2 tablespoons)

1 cup fat-free milk

1 tablespoon reduced-calorie margarine

1 tablespoon packed brown sugar

1 tablespoon water

1 tablespoon dark rum, or 1 teaspoon rum extract

1 medium banana, cut on diagonal into ¼-inch-thick slices

¼ teaspoon cinnamon

4 amaretti cookies, made into fine crumbs

1. Whisk together the pudding and milk in a medium bowl until the mixture begins to thicken slightly, about 2 minutes. Let stand 5 minutes to thicken.

2. Heat the margarine, brown sugar, water, and rum in a medium nonstick skillet over medium-high heat until the butter just begins to melt. Reduce the heat and simmer, stirring occasionally, until the mixture is blended and smooth, about 2 minutes. Add the banana slices and sprinkle with the cinnamon. Cook, stirring gently with a rubber spatula, until the bananas just begin to soften and turn golden, about 3 minutes. Remove from the heat; let cool 5 minutes.

3. Alternately layer the pudding, banana mixture, and cookie crumbs in 2 (6-ounce) parfait glasses. Serve at once or cover and refrigerate for up to several hours.

Per serving (1 parfait): 308 Cal, 6 g Fat, 7 g Sat Fat, 1 g Trans Fat, 2 mg Chol, 380 mg Sod, 55 g Carb, 2 g Fib, 6 g Prot, 188 mg Calc. *POINTS* value: 6.

Kahlua Frozen Yogurt Tartlets

MAKES 6 SERVINGS ⊗

Mini graham cracker pie crusts filled with a mixture of fat-free vanilla frozen yogurt, coffee-flavored liqueur, glazed walnuts, and mini chocolate chips make a simply delicious frozen treat. Kahlua, the most well-known coffee-flavored liqueur has been produced in Mexico for over 50 years and is easily recognized by its distinctive yellow and red label. Its complex flavor has undertones of vanilla and chocolate, making it a perfect match for the yogurt and chocolate chips. Glazed walnuts come in an 8-ounce package and can be found in the baking section of most supermarkets. If you can't find them, regular walnuts will work just as well.

2   cups fat-free vanilla
    frozen yogurt

¼   cup glazed walnuts,
    finely chopped

¼   cup mini semisweet
    chocolate chips

2   tablespoons coffee-flavored
    liqueur (kahlua)

1   (4-ounce) package mini graham
    cracker pie crusts (6 mini
    pie crusts)

2   tablespoons prepared
    chocolate sauce

1. Place the frozen yogurt, walnuts, chocolate chips, and liqueur in a food processor. Pulse until just blended, 4–5 times. Be sure not to over process or the ice cream will melt.

2. Spoon ⅓ cup of the yogurt mixture into each piecrust. Drizzle each with 1 teaspoon chocolate sauce. Freeze until firm, about 3 hours.

Per serving (1 tartlet): 263 Cal, 11 g Fat, 3 g Sat Fat, 2 g Trans Fat, 1 mg Chol, 122 mg Sod, 40 g Carb, 1 g Fib, 3 g Prot, 68 mg Calc. *POINTS* value: *6.*

Carrot Cake with Maple-Cream Frosting

MAKES 12 SERVINGS

This moist and tender carrot cake is easily mixed by hand with a wooden spoon, using only a bowl or two. Be sure to use cake flour; it is lower in protein than all-purpose flour, which assures a very tender crumb. We've spiced up the cake with cinnamon and allspice. If nutmeg is a favorite flavor, add ¼ teaspoon.

1½ cups cake flour (not self-rising)

1½ teaspoons baking powder

1   teaspoon cinnamon

½   teaspoon baking soda

½   teaspoon salt

⅛   teaspoon ground allspice

¾   cup granulated sugar

2   egg whites

1   egg yolk

2   tablespoons olive oil

1   (8-ounce) can crushed pineapple, drained, ¼ cup liquid reserved

1   cup shredded carrots (about 2 medium)

¼   cup dark raisins

4   ounces light cream cheese (Neufchâtel)

¼   cup confectioners' sugar

1   tablespoon maple syrup

1. Preheat the oven to 350°F. Spray an 8-inch square baking pan with nonstick spray.

2. Sift the flour, baking powder, cinnamon, baking soda, salt, and allspice into a medium bowl.

3. Combine the granulated sugar, egg whites, egg yolk, and oil in a large bowl until blended. Add the flour mixture and stir just until blended. Stir in the pineapple and reserved liquid, carrots, and raisins. Scrape the batter into the pan.

4. Bake until a toothpick inserted in the center comes out clean, 25–30 minutes. Cool the cake in the pan on a rack 10 minutes. Remove the cake from the pan and cool completely on the rack.

5. To prepare the frosting, beat the light cream cheese, confectioners' sugar, and maple syrup in a medium bowl until smooth. Spread on top of the cooled cake.

Per serving (¹⁄₁₂ of cake): 202 Cal, 5 g Fat, 2 g Sat Fat, 0 g Trans Fat, 25 mg Chol, 264 mg Sod, 27 g Carb, 1 g Fib, 3 g Prot, 56 mg Calc. *POINTS* value: *4.*

**Carrot Cake with
Maple-Cream Frosting**

Coconut-Chocolate Chip Ice Cream Sandwiches

MAKES 2 SERVINGS ✖

This easy dessert can be whipped up in a snap—gingersnap, that is. The spicy gingersnap cookies are filled with frozen yogurt, then rolled in coconut and chocolate chips—a match made in heaven. Make several batches and freeze them to have on hand as a fun treat for the kids or a well-deserved afternoon snack for you.

2   tablespoons sweetened flaked coconut, finely chopped

2   teaspoons mini semisweet chocolate chips

½   cup fat-free vanilla frozen yogurt

8   reduced-fat gingersnap cookies

1. Combine the coconut and chocolate chips on a sheet of wax paper.

2. Place a small baking sheet in freezer. Place 2 measuring tablespoons of the frozen yogurt on 1 cookie. Top with another cookie, gently pressing down. Working quickly, roll the cookie edges in the coconut mixture to coat then transfer to the baking sheet. Repeat with the remaining frozen yogurt, cookies, and coconut mixture to make a total of 4 sandwich cookies. Wrap each filled cookie in plastic wrap and freeze until firm, about 1 hour.

Per serving (2 sandwiches): 192 Cal, 5 g Fat, 3 g Sat Fat, 1 g Trans Fat, 1 mg Chol, 131 mg Sod, 35 g Carb, 1 g Fib, 3 g Prot, 63 mg Calc. *POINTS* value: *4*.

Coconut–Chocolate Chip
Ice Cream Sandwiches

TANGY LEMON SORBET

MAKES 4 SERVINGS

An easy-to-make, refreshing treat (no ice-cream machine required), this sorbet has just the right amount of pucker power. For the most delicious flavor, use freshly squeezed lemon juice (not bottled). Choose lemons that have thin skin and feel heavy for their size, which indicates a good amount of juice rather than lots of thick peel. When you grate the lemons, be sure to grate only the colorful part of the peel, which contains all of the flavorful oil. Avoid including the bitter white pith that is underneath.

½ cup sugar

½ cup water

1 tablespoon grated lemon zest

½ cup fresh lemon juice

1. Bring the sugar and water to a boil in a medium saucepan; boil 5 minutes. Remove from the heat and stir in the lemon zest and juice. Transfer to an 8-inch square baking dish. Let cool 15 minutes. Cover the dish with plastic wrap and place in the freezer until the lemon mixture is partially frozen, about 2 hours.

2. Transfer the sorbet to a food processor or blender. Pulse 4–5 times, just until the sorbet is smooth (be sure not to over process the sorbet or it will melt). Return the sorbet to the baking dish. Cover and freeze until firm, 3–4 hours longer.

Per serving (½ cup): 104 Cal, 0 g Fat, 0 g Sat Fat, 0 g Trans Fat, 0 mg Chol, 8 mg Sod, 27 g Carb, 0 g Fib, 0 g Prot, 5 mg Calc. *POINTS* value: *2.*

TIP For a pretty presentation, serve this sorbet in wine goblets or martini glasses and garnish with sprigs of fresh mint.

Watermelon Granita

MAKES 8 SERVINGS

This delicious icy treat is full of refreshing melon flavor and just the right amount of lime juice and freshly grated zest. A granita is more granular in texture than a sorbet due to the proportion of liquid to sugar. You can scoop the granita into glasses with an ice-cream scoop for the easiest presentation, but here is the classic way of serving this treat: Using the tip of a metal spoon, scrape the surface of the granita, transferring the icy shards to a well-chilled container. Continue until you have enough shards to fill two chilled wine glasses. Gently scoop the granita shards into the glasses and serve immediately with iced-tea spoons. For ease of preparation, buy seedless watermelon.

$^1\!/_2$	cup sugar
$^1\!/_2$	cup water
6	cups watermelon chunks
1	tablespoon grated lime zest
2	tablespoons fresh lime juice

1. Bring the sugar and water to a boil in a small saucepan; boil 5 minutes.

2. Puree the watermelon in batches in a food processor; transfer to a large bowl. Add the sugar mixture and lime zest and juice. Pour into an 8-inch square baking dish. Cover the dish with plastic wrap and place in the freezer until partially frozen, about $1^1\!/_2$ hours.

3. Remove from the freezer and stir with a fork, making sure to scrape the icy parts into the center of the dish. Cover the dish and return to the freezer until the granita is completely frozen, about 3 hours longer, stirring every 30 minutes. To serve, scoop the granita into glasses.

Per serving (generous $^1\!/_2$ cup): 86 Cal, 1 g Fat, 0 g Sat Fat, 0 g Trans Fat, 0 mg Chol, 4 mg Sod, 21 g Carb, 1 g Fib, 1 g Prot, 10 mg Calc. *POINTS* value: *2*.

———————— • ————————

TIP The purpose of stirring the granita every 30 minutes is to prevent the ice crystals from forming into a solid block. A fork is the best utensil to use as the tips of the tines easily break up the larger ice crystals. You can keep the granita covered in the freezer for up to a month and take out $^1\!/_2$ cup at a time for a refreshing treat.

Chocolate-Pecan Tuiles

CHOCOLATE-PECAN TUILES

MAKES 9 SERVINGS

These fragile and elegant cookies are named after the old-fashioned curved French roof tiles they so resemble. The cookies get their shape by being draped over a rolling pin while still hot and flexible. They are then set aside until cool and hard, which takes several minutes. Tuiles can be a little tricky to handle, as they cool quickly once out of the oven. So, work as fast as you can when transferring them to the rolling pin. If the cookies become too hard to remove from the baking sheet, return the cookies to the oven to soften for about 1 minute.

3   tablespoons sugar

2   tablespoons all-purpose flour

2   tablespoons semisweet chocolate chips, melted

1   large egg

1   tablespoon butter, melted

3   tablespoons coarsely chopped pecans

1. Preheat the oven to 400°F. Spray a large baking sheet with nonstick spray and line with parchment paper. Place the oven rack in the middle of the oven.

2. Combine the sugar, flour, melted chocolate, egg, and butter in a food processor and pulse about 10 times, until mixed well. Scrape the chocolate mixture into a small bowl.

3. Working in batches, drop rounded tablespoonfuls of the batter about 1 inch apart onto the baking sheet to make 6 cookies. With a pastry brush or narrow metal spatula, spread the batter very thinly to form 3-inch rounds. Sprinkle each round with 1/2 teaspoon of the pecans.

4. Bake until cookies are lightly browned and edges are dry, about 10 minutes. Cool cookies on baking sheet about 1 minute. Lift cookies, one at a time, with a narrow metal spatula and drape over a rolling pin to create a curved shape. Let tuiles stand until hard, about 10 minutes. Repeat with remaining batter, making a total of 18 cookies.

Per serving (2 cookies): 69 Cal, 4 g Fat, 2 g Sat Fat, 0 g Trans Fat, 27 mg Chol, 16 mg Sod, 7 g Carb, 0 g Fib, 1 g Prot, 6 mg Calc. *POINTS* value: *2*.

TIP The cookies can be made ahead and stored in an airtight container for up to three days.

PEACH MELBA SHORTCAKES

MAKES 2 SERVINGS

With this recipe, you'll be making a total of eight shortcakes but using only two. Simply wrap the unused shortcakes and freeze for up to three months. The shortcakes can be enjoyed all year long. Simply vary the fruits as the seasons change—plums, nectarines, apricots, pears, and mixed berries are all good choices.

1   large peach, halved, pitted, and cut into $^1/_8$-inch-thick slices

1   cup fresh raspberries

5   tablespoons sugar

$^1/_8$ teaspoon almond extract

$2^1/_4$ cups reduced-fat baking mix

$^2/_3$ cup fat-free milk

3   tablespoons reduced-fat margarine, melted

$^1/_4$ cup fat-free nondairy whipped topping

1   teaspoon confectioners' sugar

1. Preheat the oven to 450°F.

2. Gently toss together the peach slices, raspberries, 2 tablespoons of the sugar, and the almond extract in a medium bowl; let stand, stirring occasionally, 10 minutes. Combine the baking mix, the remaining 3 tablespoons sugar, the milk, and melted margarine in a medium bowl until a soft dough forms.

3. Lightly knead the dough 8–10 times on a lightly floured surface. Roll out the dough $^1/_2$-inch thick. Cut out rounds with a lightly floured $2^1/_2$-inch cutter. Place about 1 inch apart on an ungreased baking sheet. Gather up the dough trimmings, re-roll, and cut out dough rounds making a total of 8 rounds.

4. Bake the shortcakes until the tops are golden and a toothpick inserted in the center comes out clean, 10–12 minutes. Transfer to a rack to cool completely. Wrap and freeze 6 shortcakes to use another time.

5. With a serrated knife, cut the remaining 2 shortcakes horizontally in half. Place the bottoms on dessert plates. Spoon the peach mixture over each shortcake bottom and top each with 2 tablespoons whipped topping. Cover with the top half of the shortcakes and sprinkle with the confectioners' sugar.

Per serving (1 shortcake, ¾ cup peach mixture, 2 tablespoons topping): 355 Cal, 6 g Fat, 1 g Sat Fat, 1 g Trans Fat, 0 mg Chol, 574 mg Sod, 69 g Carb, 7 g Fib, 6 g Prot, 90 mg Calc. *POINTS* value: *7.*

CAPPUCCINO BISCOTTI

MAKES 12 SERVINGS

Biscotti have become as familiar to Americans as chocolate chip cookies. These twice-baked treats are liked for several reasons: They are easy to prepare, they store very well, they can be made in large numbers, and flavored in a variety of ways. These biscotti are very similar to classic Italian biscotti in that they aren't nearly as rich as some versions. They are meant to be rather hard, so they can be dunked into vin santo or espresso without fear of the cookies falling apart. Italians really love their biscotti. They are enjoyed for breakfast, as an afternoon snack with espresso, or after a meal with wine. Mangia!

¾ cup all-purpose flour

3 tablespoons unsweetened cocoa powder

2 teaspoons instant espresso powder

2 teaspoons cinnamon

½ teaspoon baking powder

¼ teaspoon salt

½ cup sugar

1 large egg

½ teaspoon vanilla extract

¼ cup coarsely chopped pecans

1. Preheat the oven to 350°F. Line a baking sheet with foil; lightly spray with nonstick spray.

2. Sift the flour, cocoa, espresso powder, cinnamon, baking powder, and salt into a medium bowl. Whisk together the sugar, egg, and vanilla in a small bowl until frothy. Add the egg mixture to the flour mixture and stir with a wooden spoon just until a dough forms. Stir in the pecans.

3. Gather dough with lightly floured hands and transfer to a lightly floured surface. Roll the dough into a 2 x 8-inch log. Transfer the log to the baking sheet and shape into a log that is about ¾ inch high and 2 inches wide.

4. Bake until firm to the touch, 20–25 minutes. Transfer the log to a cutting board and cool 5–7 minutes. With a serrated knife, cut into 12 (¼-inch-thick) slices. Arrange the slices, cut-side down, on the baking sheet.

5. Reduce the oven temperature to 300°F. Bake the biscotti 10 minutes, then turn them over and bake until very dry and slightly crisp, about 10 minutes longer. Transfer the biscotti to a rack and cool completely. They will continue to dry out as they cool.

Per serving (1 biscotti): 89 Cal, 3 g Fat, 0 g Sat Fat, 0 g Trans Fat, 18 mg Chol, 75 mg Sod, 16 g Carb, 1 g Fib, 2 g Prot, 23 mg Calc. *POINTS* value: *2.*

ABOUT OUR RECIPES

We make every effort to ensure that you will have success with our recipes. For best results and for nutritional accuracy, please keep the following guidelines in mind:

- All recipes feature approximate nutritional information; our recipes are analyzed for Calories (Cal), Total Fat (Fat), Saturated Fat (Sat Fat), Trans Fat (Trans Fat), Cholesterol (Chol), Sodium (Sod), Carbohydrates (Carb), Dietary Fiber (Fib), Protein (Prot), and Calcium (Calc).

- Nutritional information for recipes that include meat, fish, and poultry are based on cooked skinless boneless portions (unless otherwise stated), with the fat trimmed as specified in the recipe.

- All recipes include *POINTS* values based on the Weight Watchers FlexPoints Food System. *POINTS* values are calculated from a proprietary formula that takes into account calories, total fat, and dietary fiber.

- Before serving, divide foods—including any vegetables, sauce, or accompaniments—into portions of equal size according to the designated number of servings per recipe.

- Any substitutions made to the ingredients will alter the "Per serving" nutritional information and may affect the *POINTS* value.

- Additionally, substituting fat-free foods for any low-fat ingredients specified in a recipe may affect the consistency, texture, or flavor of the finished dish.

- If you prefer to avoid using alcohol in any recipe, you may substitute an equal amount of water, broth, or juice.

- It is implied that all greens in recipes should be washed or rinsed.

- All herbs called for are fresh, not dried, unless otherwise specified.

DRY AND LIQUID MEASUREMENT EQUIVALENTS

If you are converting the recipes in this book to metric measurements, use the following chart as a guide.

TEASPOONS	TABLESPOONS	CUPS	FLUID OUNCES
3 teaspoons	1 tablespoon		½ fluid ounce
6 teaspoons	2 tablespoons	⅛ cup	1 fluid ounce
8 teaspoons	2 tablespoons plus 2 teaspoons	⅙ cup	
12 teaspoons	4 tablespoons	¼ cup	2 fluid ounces
15 teaspoons	5 tablespoons	⅓ cup minus 1 teaspoon	
16 teaspoons	5 tablespoons plus 1 teaspoon	⅓ cup	
18 teaspoons	6 tablespoons	¼ cup plus 2 tablespoons	3 fluid ounces
24 teaspoons	8 tablespoons	½ cup	4 fluid ounces
30 teaspoons	10 tablespoons	½ cup plus 2 tablespoons	5 fluid ounces
32 teaspoons	10 tablespoons plus 2 teaspoons	⅔ cup	
36 teaspoons	12 tablespoons	¾ cup	6 fluid ounces
42 teaspoons	14 tablespoons	1 cup minus 1 tablespoon	7 fluid ounces
45 teaspoons	15 tablespoons	1 cup minus 1 tablespoon	
48 teaspoons	16 tablespoons	1 cup	8 fluid ounces

VOLUME	
¼ teaspoon	1 milliliter
½ teaspoon	2 milliliters
1 teaspoon	5 milliliters
1 tablespoon	15 milliliters
2 tablespoons	30 milliliters
3 tablespoons	45 milliliters
¼ cup	60 milliliters
⅓ cup	80 milliliters
½ cup	120 milliliters
⅔ cup	160 milliliters
¾ cup	175 milliliters
1 cup	240 milliliters
1 quart	950 milliliters

LENGTH	
1 inch	25 millimeters
1 inch	2.5 centimeters

WEIGHT	
1 ounce	30 grams
¼ pound	120 grams
½ pound	240 grams
1 pound	480 grams

OVEN TEMPERATURE

250°F	120°C	400°F	200°C
275°F	140°C	425°F	220°C
300°F	150°C	450°F	230°C
325°F	160°C	475°F	250°C
350°F	180°C	500°F	260°C
375°F	190°C	525°F	270°C

Note: Measurement of less than ⅛ teaspoon is considered a dash or a pinch. Metric volume measurements are approximate.

INDEX

NOTES

NOTES